THE RIVER ROOST
Stories of the Allegan Forest

from the letters of Glenn E. McNitt
(1947-1970)

Compiled and Edited
by
Carol Eichinger

Illustrated
by
Judy Finnegan

THROUGH THE DOOR PUBLISHING CO.
Portage, Michigan

Printed by
Superior Colour Graphics, Kalamazoo, Michigan

First Edition
Text Copyright 2001, by Carol Eichinger
and Myrna McNitt
Illustrations 2001, by Judy Finnegan

With support from

michigan council for
arts and cultural affairs

ISBN 0-9709373-0-X

For purchasing information e-mail:
EICH 616@AOL.com

Through The Door Publishing Co.
3414 Fleetwood Drive, Portage, MI 49024

Dedicated to the grandchildren of

Glenn and Cecile McNitt:

Susan and Kelly,
Randy and Lisa,
Kim and Michael

and to grandchildren everywhere.

TABLE OF CONTENTS

List of Illustrations

DAYS AT RIVER ROOST

That house in the Allegan Forest still stands.
It is through the woods at the end of the gravel road.
It overlooks the wide pasture which
wanders down to the gravel pit and
watches the Kalamazoo River flow past
at the bottom of the hill's gentle slope.
We were children there.
That pebble-stone house,
its fireplace, the stuffed bear cub,
the old barn and chicken coop,
the one-room school house just beyond the forest edge
held all we knew
when we were just Kay and Carol, Ted and Terry.
River Roost is still there in the hearts of its children.

So many memories. There were so many people
and so many stories. Across the open back porch with the
big metal swing, into the house and up the few steps into
the kitchen, suddenly it was, "Hello, Aunt Cecile; hi,
Uncle Glenn!" The kitchen smelled of chicken and
dumplings; and the big pots in the oven were full.
Potatoes and vegetables were on top of the stove and the
salads were already on the table. Uncle Glenn's homemade sweet rolls or braided breads, or even sour dough

breads were on the side table smelling so wonderful. Everyone was there, talking, laughing, moving chairs and putting things on the table. It was Sunday dinner at the Roost and we were all there.

When the big dinner was over, we had a mountain of dishes to do! Oh, not just dishes; we had silverware and glasses and cups and saucers and serving dishes big and small and pots and pans of all sizes and shapes! We were organized into a small army of workers to wash and dry every item and put the kitchen back in order. Our mothers and aunts did most of the supervising, this task usually beginning with my mother, Aunt Sylvia to everyone else, announcing that it was time to play "FitzPatrick." A nursing friend of hers from Detroit who had five children had trained them to pick up their own table setting, plate and silverware and glass, and carry it all out to the sink to be rinsed. My mother was so delighted with how quickly a table could be cleared after a meal with this method that she could be counted on to begin the cleanup session with her "Let's all play FitzPatrick." She always giggled after she said it too. So we all carried the dishes to the kitchen; an older child, usually Chum (his name is really Glenn like his father but we called him Chum in those days) or next in line Ted would wash and all the younger ones were handed a dish towel to dry. Then Kay or Myrna, the younger sisters of Chum and Ted, would turn on the phonograph and put on a record of a musical popular on New York's Broadway. While singing the choruses to *Oklahoma*, *My Fair Lady*, and *South Pacific*, we tried to keep up with the dishes.

River Roost was the farm which Glenn and Cecile McNitt bought after World War II. They weren't really farmers; he was a salesman and she was a legal secretary. They wanted to make a special home for their four young children to grow and thrive in and even to cherish when they were grown, so the farm in the forest seemed to be the perfect setting. They both loved trying new (some thought crazy!) ideas and they both loved people; consequently, there were the chicken and egg farming years, the sheep farming years, the pig (whew!) farming years, and always there were relatives, his relatives and her relatives, and there were many friends and neighbors. If the farm could provide fresh garden vegetables, fresh meat, fresh milk and money for other expenses plus be a wonderful place for the whole family (aunts and uncles, sisters and brothers and cousins big and little), it would be a treasure. So this family found its treasure and lived there for over twenty years. Glenn saved many of the stories of his family and relatives and wrote them down as letters which he lovingly referred to as his "Historie of River Roost." It is these letters which he sent to the extended family in his later years and are now recorded here for you, dear reader. Aunt Selma brought a large shoe box up from her basement one warm summer evening and said to me, "Here are your Uncle Glenn's letters about the farm. I hope you can put these together for the grandchildren to read. I know it may take a while. It took Katherine Marshall nine years to write *Christy* from her aunt's letters." There were in that box over thirty envelopes each containing between four and six letters. And so the stories are told here again. The farm did provide the fresh vegetables, meat, eggs, and milk, and it did provide a wonderful place for a large family to gather; but its real treasure now lies in the memories and the love that we all have from our days at River Roost.

Mischa named the farm the "River Roost." He had been a Russian aristocrat who had escaped his homeland during the Russian Revolution of 1917. Leaving his family and crossing eastern Europe, he arrived in Paris where he stayed for several years. He met an American woman there whom he married and they then came to Holland in western Michigan. Mischa loved riding horses and fishing and hunting, so his wife bought the large farm in Allegan County along the banks of the Kalamazoo River for him. It was his hunting and fishing lodge. But after World War II ended, his health began to fail, and so he sold the 127-acre farm in the forest to Glenn and Cecile, and our enchanted days there began. The stuffed black bear cub, shot in British Columbia on one of his hunting ventures and now standing in the living room alcove near the huge fieldstone fireplace, was a reminder to us all of Mischa's days at River Roost. Now I will let Glenn tell the tales. His first letter was written introducing himself and his family to a gentleman from Texas. This letter serves as an excellent introduction to this work as well.

Carol Eichinger

Glenn At The Typewriter

IN MAKING YOUR ACQUAINTANCE

My dear Albert Bergman,

Forgetting, as you see, all formalities, I'll rush right into this answer to your "Dad, he can type better than you!" (from my daughter) recent letter. What a pleasant surprise I received when I collected our usual mess of advertising material which I do every day promptly at 1:30 P.M. to find your interesting and entertaining letter standing sharply out against a background of bills and fly-ers. Last night a former neighbor of our family, but wait – you will need some background before I scurry headlong

Ted, Kay, Glenn, Chum, Cecile and Myrna

into something quite unintelligible without proper preparation, you will agree, before I can indulge you with a most strange co-incidence which occurred on the same day that your letter arrived. Before moving to Holland after my forced retirement, we lived on a farm nestled along the banks of the Kalamazoo River—a solid mile of river frontage, thirty cleared acres and one hundred acres of scrub, regrowth woodland. It was a wonderful place to have a garden, a horse, a couple of cows, chickens, and, of course, children: four of them—two boys and two girls, plus two dogs, and uncountable cats. All in all, it was a good place to live and a good place to raise a family (which we did with a zest), large enough for friends and relatives to continually swarm in and out; for over twenty years it was a meeting place for our clan. Our house was rather large —four bedrooms with one full and two half baths; but we were ONE MILE from our closest neighbor. One of those neighbors and very close friends was a family by the name, believe it or not, of Bergman. Mrs. Bergman and one of her daughters, Mary, came to call on us the very night that I received your letter! They originally came from Germany, that portion which borders Holland, or rather, the Netherlands, the district close to Gronegen and Drenthe. So, you see, your letter, coming as it did, provided no little excitement and provided considerable conversation.

Most of my ancestors, I suppose, have been in this country since the first white man attempted (successfully) to cheat an Indian by offering to trade him a bottle of homemade whiskey (I did have an ancestor who operated his own still) for thousands of acres of land. The name McNitt has travelled a long way since it left bonnie Scotland where it started out as MacNaughton, descending to MacNaught, McNutt, MacNitt, and finally McNitt. Living, as we did, in an all-Dutch community, it was not at all uncommon for the local residents to call us VanNitt, and even for a while, during the time that we raised ducks, VanDUCK! I suppose that eventually it will end up as just plain Nitt!

My wife is a third generation German descendant and she is a secretary working in law offices in Allegan, the county seat. This is a smallish community of perhaps seven or eight thousand people, about a twenty-five mile drive from our home, and there it is that she is still working on her first million. I retired at 62 after a lifetime of sales work because of seldom-heard-of Paget's disease, a rather painful affliction but still one that I have learned to live with, or at least to maintain a reasonable semblance of sanity by doing just this: typing out reams and reams of nonsense for the most part, a so-called Historie of River Roost (the name of our farm). I must admit, however, that my collection of notes accumulated over many years

Glenn and Cecile

has often come under the censorship of my ever cautious wife.

Many things fill my days now, but my main interest is, well, there is no other name for it, hoarding books, a habit of many years which has resulted in a small library of perhaps three or four thousand volumes, good, bad and just plain ordinary books, but still, none that I would part with! At present I am engaged in trying to index our library, but I am finding it to be quite a task. Yes, it is true that I am a history buff and I have accumulated several volumes on our Revolutionary and Civil Wars. I have also acquired the amusing, but often expensive habit, shared by all the rest of the family, of acquiring and refinishing antique furniture. We then put our completed projects into a house already replete with too much old, scarred and abused, but well-loved pieces from past generations. In this, I am not altogether blameless since the rest of the family keeps prodding me on. In addition to all of this, I bake bread and I write very weak verse. I get many "mmmmm's" for the bread and many groans for the verse. You are really not too far away, so perhaps one day we will meet. Now there's a nice thought.

Informally yours,
Glenn E. McNitt

HOW, WHEN, AND WHY WE PURCHASED RIVER ROOST

My dear ones,

Vague and troublesome desires had for some considerable time been bothering both my spouse and me when, as my eyes roamed over the classified section of our newspaper, I came across an unusual advertisement. It captured and fascinated my imagination with the mental picture of that "Good Life." I knew that this was IT. About the middle of May in that happy year of 1947, I bundled Chummy, our firstborn, into the seat of our Nash and leaving Grand Rapids behind us, I drove out M-21 to the Gold Estate in Holland, Michigan. There I met the caretaker and I explained to him that I had come in answer to the "Farm for Sale" ad. The owner of the farm which had caught my interest was not at home, but "Albert" agreed to leave the four acres of lawn which he was mowing and drive us about ten miles or so to see the property which his employer had advertised. Already, it seemed, we were rising in the world, since, following his suggestion, we left our unwashed Nash and climbed into an extra large, finely equipped and upholstered Chrysler station wagon, glistening under a fresh wax job. "Albert" drove us over winding country roads to a large pebble-stuccoed house located far back in the woods of the Allegan

State Forest, on the banks of the wild Kalamazoo River. This, we were told, was the hunting lodge of "Mischa" Thorgevesky, formerly a Russian Count. He had escaped his native land during the frightening days of the Russian Revolution (especially frightening for the aristocracy!) but he was now safely married to Margaret Dicky Gold, who was the widow of the railroad air brake baron and so inherited his fortune. It was she who had bought the farm which we were now seeing and had presented it to Mischa for his personal use. Mrs. Thorgevesky at this time was visiting in New York, and Mischa was taking advantage of her absence to sell this property in order to secure the cash with which he might purchase a fast race horse to add to his stable of trotting horses. He was hoping to augment the allowance which Mrs. Thorgevesky advanced to him with the winnings of the new horse. Furthermore, since the rationing which had resulted from World War II was no longer in effect, the farm was not needed to supply additional food stuffs not covered by stamps, and so the farm had outlived its usefulness for him. Albert was quite chatty on the drive out to the farm!

Chummy had fallen asleep in the back of the station wagon and after awakening him, we started to roam through the fully furnished house. The furniture would be included with the sale. With all this before me, amazing thoughts raced through my mind. I was enthralled, not only with the house, but also with the apparent possibilities for chicken farming which could take me off the road as a salesman and allow me to stay at home with my family, especially since we had one child with a mysterious ailment at the time. "Get that boy out in the sun and keep him there!" had been the instruction from the doctor who had taken care of Teddy, our second-born. He was absorbing almost constant blood transfusions. It seemed that his white blood cells were rapidly eating up his red cells, and we were deathly afraid that he had leukemia at the time. Fortunately, he didn't have it, but with all those thoughts and secret ambitions running around my head, it took little effort to convince my dear wife Cecile that she should also go and see how desirable it would be if we were all to move out to the "River Roost." One trip through the house, peeking under beds and bedspreads and into cupboards, peering into all the corners and at Mischa's coat of arms above the arch, studying the stuffed deer head over the fireplace and the bear cub, also stuffed, in the alcove of the living room, running fingers lightly over the keys of the grand piano at the far end of the living room (Mischa was quite a singer in Paris during the 20's while en route to America, according to Albert, and this is where he met his American wife), and poking around all the other places that women poke into, she put her seal of approval on the purchase and so in only a few days River Roost was ours—with a mortgage, of course. When Mrs. Thorgevesky returned from New York, the sale had advanced to the point where only her signature was needed. She wasn't too happy about parting with the farm, but since this was what Mischa wanted, she accorded her approval. Thus it was that by the middle of June we were cultivating the already planted garden and feeding some hastily purchased chickens and we were embarking on a totally new life— and thereby hung many, many tales.

Are they all true, you ask? Of course, of course!

That's why they must be told.

GEM

THE NEIGHBORHOOD

...Or an informative little letter containing a few odd observations and hopefully helpful instructions on the management of a good neighbor policy.

My dear ones,

Generally we were given a cautiously reserved approval when we first moved into the River Road neighborhood. There was very much that these clannish people of Dutch heritage wanted to know about the McNitts before they would fully accept them as proper God-fearing neighbors with whom they might safely associate. As Lutherans, we were acknowledged as a church-going family mainly through their knowledge of Dr. Walter Maier of national radio fame (The Lutheran Hour) whom they admired. However, according to good Dutch upbringing one must not, under any consideration, work on Sunday; one must never, never drink alcohol of any kind; one must attend church regularly, preferably two times each Sabbath. Living secluded, far back in the forest availed little in these matters. We were always slyly told if our car was not observed churchward bound on a Sunday. But, slowly, we learned how to manipulate these matters and the barriers of religion and their skeptical regard of "city folk" fell, and so one by one, we began to receive calls from our neighbors.

A neighborly call followed a rigid pattern. Your neighbors must always be notified in advance before you made an appearance at their door. A spontaneous or casual call was a horrible breach of etiquette, and consequently we never heard, "If I had known you were going to call, I'd have baked a cake." No indeed, just "dropping in" was

26

not at all acceptable. Not only must a notification be given, but a regular pattern of calls had to be followed. "It's your turn now," was an inflexible rule. Oh, yes, dancing and card playing were, of course, highly frowned upon, so a call was just that—a call, where you sat around and muttered inanities, making profound observations on the weather and crops and finally ate a "lap" lunch which consisted of a sandwich, a piece of cake and a couple of cookies, all on one plate along with a cup of coffee, all of which you precariously balanced on your knee. Incidentally, a call was never recognized officially unless both husband and wife were present. I couldn't get away with sending Cecile and thus claiming that our "turn" had been made. Still, all and all, these neighbors of ours were wonderful people and once we were accepted, they were constantly conferring innumerable favors upon us, and we learned to truly love them,

as I do you,

GEM

THERE IS A TIME TO PLANT

To every thing there is a season, and a time to every purpose under the heavens. There is a ...time to plant, and a time to pluck up that which is planted. *Ecclesiastes* 3

My dear ones,

Under Cecile's tutelage we early learned that when the moon was new and full, it was the proper time to plant our garden. Make no mistake about the right time of the moon—it's important! "I don't care what you think. It is NOT superstition. If you don't plant at the right time of

Rhubarb

the moon, you won't have a garden! Just you wait and see!" Thus spoke she of the green thumb. And the right time of the moon was Memorial Day. And that was the day, year after year that our garden was planted. It was also the time of the year that we recruited free labor. Not only our own family, but every relative that we could cajole or dragoon into our service was given a tool of choice and a package of seeds and then pointed toward our garden. This was the auspicious time of the year when the moon was exactly right to drop our seeds into the well prepared,

Eggplant

warm earth; and then we could sit back and watch them battle it out with lush weeds and crab grass. With a little cultivating and a little hand weeding and a lot of hoeing we usually were able to keep ahead, or at least, abreast of the weeds and we ended up with a good garden, a bountiful one. Strawberry plants and rhubarb plants bordered the eastern side of the garden, and a double row of red raspberries ran the full length of the western side, while in the center area, perhaps 200 by 60 feet, we planted and transplanted all of our hungry hopes for an edible year.

It is truly amazing how many pickles just a few creeping vines will produce. But what is more surprising and amazing is how many wax or green beans a few short rows will yield. With the appearance of the first bean we would pick and pick until everybody concerned including our freezer was glutted; and then the plants would show new blossoms and start bearing all over again! It was at this time when our good neighbors would bring to us a full pail of freshly picked beans! "Hope you can use a few beans."

From our garden was harvested also quite a different product. Crawling along on hands and knees while weeding, we frequently found Indian arrowheads, and over a period of years the children accumulated a very satisfactory collection. So many arrowheads found here suggested that on this site, a meadow next to the river with a forest surrounding it all, there most likely had been an Indian camp or maybe even an Indian war years earlier. At least it made for good conversation and questions from the children while little hands pulled all those weeds. "Are there any Indians in the woods now?" Sunburn and tan, sweat and dirt, arrowheads and fresh food—that was our garden—and it was GOOD.

With dirt under my nails,
GEM

Squash

31

PEGGY AND BEAUTY AND DAISY AND PRINCESS

In making a series of new bovine friends and thus improving the quality and quantity of our food supply, we find that the laws of motion are immutable; and that since the theory that, while for every action there is an equal and usually opposite reaction, the stark reality is that what goes in the front must be shoveled from the rear and while this may be good for the garden, it surely makes for an ouchy back!

My dear ones,

Peggy and Beauty were sleek black Jersey heifers and they were the first cows we ever owned. This ownership started a long and arduous bondage to the gutter directly behind where they were stalled in the barn. We were easily enticed into bidding on these well groomed animals by a glib auctioneer who claimed that since they had already been bred and would soon "freshen," either one of them would make an ideal family cow. We were easily led down this primrosed path because we hoped that owning our own cow would not only help the perpetually strained family budget, but at the same time it would give the children

Daisy

far richer milk than that which we were purchasing at the store. All farm auctions are rapid fire affairs geared to keeping all bidders on their toes. The incredible yarn about the man who scratched his itching ear at one of these affairs and then heard the auctioneer shout "SOLD" is no fiction. We were bidding on one animal and discovered that the acceptance of our bid meant that we had just purchased TWO! We had ample room not only in the barn but in our hearts as well for both of these animals, but this double purchase necessitated a lot of scrounging around to find the cash to cover the check which we drew for their purchase. This bit of scrounging can be verified by our ever loving and helpful Aunt Ruth, my dear Cecile's older sister. So with considerable antici-pation we awaited that wonderful and mysterious event when either Peggy or Beauty would "freshen." The ani-mals, not the least bit concerned, went their happy way, grazing and exploring the west end of our farm bordered by a quickly and crazily repaired fence. Thank the good Lord for bailing wire! Ah, yes, I remember it well!

After a few days it was a moot question of who would come into our world first: our fourth child which we expected in September or a new calf. Peggy turned up missing one morning and we knew before we started to search for her that she had won. Near the edge of the woods which bordered our pasture, we found a proud cow busily engaged in the process of cleaning up her newborn calf. With an indescribable thrill, I picked up this warm, wet, unresisting little animal and carried it back to the barn with Peggy blatting and bellowing behind me. Keeping ahead of the protesting mother, I decided to call this first calf of ours Earl, a bit of word play since the calf was early, having beaten into this world Myrna Lee by three weeks. When the whole family rushed to the barn to inspect the newcomer, I found, much to my embarrassment, that I had been a bit hasty in the choice of names. HE was a SHE! We changed the name Earl to Pearl, a simple and quick way out of my red-faced predicament. A couple of months later, when all of our animals were ensconced in the barn for the winter, a season which arrived early that year and stayed late, Beauty presented us with another heifer calf, and so we found ourselves milking two cows, the old fashioned hard way. For a few months before we decided to wean the calves, we were engaged in a race to see who could get the milking done first, those cold-handed humans or the warm-lipped calves. I think that we got our share, or at least all that we needed.

The act of milking, while not a particularly difficult job, if one has strong hands, can become a tedious task mostly because of the demanding regularity. You don't milk at six o'clock one morning and nine o'clock the next morning if you expect to get reasonably good milk production and keep your cows healthy. It is not like turning on the water tap and drawing off as much liquid as you need. You must maintain a certain regularity with little flexibility in your time schedule if you want to keep yourself and your cows happy. With this matter of regularity settled, we found that the flow of milk from two cows astounded us. Every surplus pan plus a few borrowed ones were filled with milk while we waited for the cream to rise. How quickly we found ourselves, in operating our own private dairy, entered upon a race to see which one of us could foist upon our relatives the largest quantity of surplus milk. Little nephew Terry, raised in town, asked, "Why don't you get your milk from the milkman who comes to our house instead of from those cows?" We weren't to be persuaded! When every crock, pan, jar, and dish was filled with milk, we skimmed off the cream as a first step which was to lead to many more possibilities. We made butter. We festooned every dessert with whipped cream. We made cottage cheese, and from this we went on to a more noble project: that of manufacturing for our own use that delicately flavored and delicious item known as cooked cheese. While the end result was well worth the effort, the process was a "stinky one," as the children noted. We bought a family-sized pasteurizer and then pasteurized all the milk for our own consumption. When our capacity for all milk products reached a limit, we bought a couple of pigs to take care of the overflow and thus we solved the problem of the surplus by a simple process of conversion (turning it into pork)!

Shortly after a cow freshens, she should be bred again to insure the minimum period of low milk production. This we were told, and this advice we attempted to follow, wanting in all our farm ventures to be as correct and as knowledgeable as possible. For this particular labor of love, one of our neighbors volunteered the services of his bull. Consequently, when that time of the month, which is a normal biological pattern for all cows, arrived, we backed our old panel truck up to a convenient spot on the barn hill and attempted to induce Beauty to step aboard. Beauty, however, was not stepping. To load a thousand-pound cow, who isn't particularly interested in being loaded on any regular flatbed truck, is a herculean task, but such a task is mere child's play when compared to the loading of such a cow into a panel truck. This loading process makes it necessary for the cow to stoop slightly to gain entrance. Beauty not only wouldn't stoop; she didn't want to go any way, any how, or in any manner. Not to be overcome in this battle of wills, wits, and brawn by the inferior intellect of a mere cow, we arrived at a compromise. A compromise usually indicates a meeting of the minds, so this was only a half compromise, since Beauty just stood still and agreed to nothing. We couldn't get her to agree to a ride within the truck, so I decided to securely tie her to the back bumper and then I proceeded in low gear as slowly as possible, literally pulling this most recalcitrant of animals behind us!

It was a good two miles to our neighbor's farm. For a mile and a half our pilgrimage went reasonably well. At that point, however, Beauty without consulting us decided to stop and rest, which she did by simply bracing her feet against the pull of the truck. But the truck kept right on going. The rope broke. I stopped the truck and glanced out. Beauty looked at me balefully with red-flecked eyes for a moment and then she let out a tremendous bellow of disgust and turning tail, she started to run. She ran every step of the way home with never a backward glance or pause until she reached the barnyard. This was the point

38

in our farming career where we became staunch advocates of artificial breeding.

We arranged to keep up with the flow of milk until our pigs matured and were helped on the way to the destination of all pigs. No longer able to cope with the quantities of milk derived from two family cows, we sold one of our black Jerseys to a nearby farmer with a commercial herd of milk cattle. We kept Peggy because she was the easier one to milk. With Peggy, you could really take hold of your work, whereas, with Beauty, it was a thumb and first finger job. Clear? A few months after the disposition of Beauty, a financial crisis arose. Actually, it wasn't a real crisis, but rather one of the ordinary up-and-down conditions which frequently plagued us. This was one of the downs. Anyway, we sold Peggy, and then promptly regretted it. While it may be a trifle inconvenient to have too much milk, it is a downright burden with four children not to have any. So, riding on the crest of one of our ups we began to look around for a replacement for Peggy. It was at another farm auction that we discovered and bought Daisy. Daisy was a brown Jersey with a glossy hide and a most gentle disposition and we all became inordinately fond of her. This little brown cow immediately became the boss of the few feeder cattle which were run-

39

ning in our pasture at that time. She ruled these larger animals autocratically, permitting no challenge to her authority. She led; the rest of the animals followed. For three years she ruled our small herd with complete authority and also commanded from us unwavering love and affection. Then this unfortunate animal had a miscarriage and lost her calf, an accident which left her with milk fever. Every two hours we had to medicate our poor ill Daisy, using a block and tackle to move her from side to side by the use of slings. Our small efforts were quite useless and the tears rolled unabashedly down our cheeks when a truck came to take our good friend away.

After Daisy came Princess. Princess, we were assured when we bought her, was gentle, a good producer, well-mannered; in fact, she was such an exceptional cow that her owners wanted to be very, very sure that she was going to a good and kind family before they would part with her. Such an animal would indeed be a prize and we went to great length to assure her owners that we met the necessary qualifications to own such a paragon of a family cow. We finally passed the examination and were accorded the privilege of purchasing Princess. Oh, she was everything that her former owners claimed with but one small exception. She kicked! She kicked only, of course, when we milked her. At all other times she was a perfect lady, bright and attentive to our every desire, but it was impossible to complete a milking unless she either kicked over the milk pail or, setting her hoof comfortably inside it, she refused to budge. Never was a milking session completed without milk being spilled in the gutter. Eventually we purchased an invention which was marketed to frustrate such animals as our Princess: a set of 'kickers,' a chain device which prevents a cow from raising her feet. We never were able to milk Princess without her 'kickers!' We learned many lessons from Peggy and Beauty, Daisy and Princess; and their milk was oh so good.

Bye, for now, my black and brown cows,

GEM

THE GUINEA HEN

In which the sins of omission are exposed and the hard lessons of farm life are learned.

My dear ones,

When we first took possession of River Roost, there stood a very ancient and decrepit corn crib over near a building which apologetically called itself a garage. This corn crib, like the tower of Pisa, leaned earthward far more than the law of gravity should allow. The roof sagged and the floor had rotted through, making it a hazard to man and beast; and we all agreed that it must be torn down at once. Here it was that our Teddy found a nesting guinea hen.

Since everything was new and strange with even the air smelling of adventure, our kind, artless little boy reached out to pet this innocuous looking lady guinea hen when she, in righteous anger, promptly flew off the nest and circled his head, flapping her wings and dive bombing toward his face. She continued her assault until she had driven him out of the ancient building and sent him on a dead run toward the safety of the house. We delayed the destruction of the corn crib until this half-wild mother hatched out her eggs, watching her, meanwhile, between the slats of the rotting building. In her angry flurry when she was furiously driving barefooted Teddy shrieking into his mother's arms, she was a far better parent than she was the morning when she led her tiny, newly hatched babies out into the cold wetness of the morning dew. It was early in the morning when we made our daily check and discovered the missing hen. Her trail was all too easy to follow because the little dead bodies of the frail, newborn creatures unable to cope with the simple dangers to which they were exposed by a thoughtless mother were all over the ground.

'Tis difficult learning the ways of farm creatures,
but I remain your hopeful farmer.

GEM

LITTLE FEATHERED WATCHDOGS

Wherein we gird ourselves to do valiant battle but more often than not, we are outwitted by certain noble and nervous feathered watchdogs.

My dear ones,

Guineas awaited us when first we arrived at River Roost to make it our home, and they gave us a most raucous welcome. The peculiarly noisy and discordant, almost human cry of a disturbed guinea is perhaps the most penetrating and irresistible, captivating call of any domesticated bird. While guineas have lived on American farms from the time of the early colonies, there has always been in my mind a large question whether or not this strange bird could truthfully be called domesticated. They gladly welcome man's offering of scientifically blended chicken mash of the popular grains, corn, wheat, and oats, but they disdain to roost as a chicken does on a comfortable roost, preferring instead the high peak of the barn roof or the topmost branches of a tree for their nightly resting place. They march scornfully past our carefully prepared chicken nests and fly over the fence to hide their eggs in some cleverly concealed spot. At the appearance of anything that is slightly different and disturbing to their regular pattern of life, they raise their voices in inharmonious warning and thus they well earn the title, a feathered watchdog. Believe me, when a guinea shrieks, you had better "git out and look" since they are telling you something of vital importance. While they will eventually tolerate you, they will never completely accept you. Although they have an abiding distrust of everything on a farm and they find all visitors very offensive, they are interesting to watch. They are cute and clever. They are also good to eat, if and when you can catch them. By the way, when your host is carving one at the dining room table, never ask for white meat, for the flesh of this succulent bird is all dark.

If, when raising guineas, you feel that you might possibly be feeding more males than females and that this is not an economically sound practice, leave well enough alone. Do not try to capture and sex your guineas. If by some peculiar quirk of fortune you were able to outwit them and accomplish this almost impossible chore of catching a few members of your flock, you would still face a problem that has long stumped the experts. There are no easily recognizable characteristics to differentiate between the male and the female. Guineas are almost impossible to sex. Leave them alone. You won't make any money on them anyway; they are just interesting to have roaming around.

In the spring, a guinea hen will lay a clutch of eggs numbering from ten to fifteen, all that she can comfortably cover. She is very ingenious in hiding her nest, but if discovered, she will protect it with her life if need be. If her battle plan isn't successful, she will call for her husband to help her. I learned early to watch my unprotected head when disturbing a nesting guinea hen, for she will most certainly fly at you prepared to fight to the finish. Unfortunately when the "hatch comes off" and the mother guinea hen proudly starts out in the early morning with her brood of newly hatched keets, nature will take its toll. The tiny creatures can't stand the dampness of the early morning dew, a fact either ignored by the mother guinea or one that is totally lacking in her otherwise over-developed instincts. So, this early morning dew, which is so necessary to plant life, is a vicious killer to the tiny keets. It is actually surprising how few keets a mother guinea can raise to full maturity.

To combat this terrific mortality I have often fought with the mother guinea in order to steal her eggs for placement under one of our broody Rock hens. This, however, didn't work very well either, for while a chicken is a perfect mother for chickens, she hasn't the haziest notion of how to properly raise a keet. When she is faced with the problem of raising a brood of tiny semi-wild keets, she is temperamentally maladjusted. When the eggs are hatched, she takes the children out to forage for food, and clucking in a true maternal fashion, she attempts to teach her youngsters how to scratch for food. While her heart may be in her work, the heart of a baby guinea is not. They will follow her obediently, but when she starts to scratch, death stalks the land! I have seen a chicken scratching for her brood and with never a backward glance toss one keet after another several feet away from her with each scratch of her unsuspecting feet. The little half-ounce creatures can't take this rough treatment, and it is very painful for me to watch them fly through the air before they even learn to fly. For, you see, guineas do not scratch.

We have also attempted to raise them along with baby chicks, under an electric brooder, with reasonable success. However, as they begin to increase in size they cannot compete with the baby chickens eating at the feed tray, and they are constantly being shoved aside by their more aggressive relatives. Our best success was attained by capturing the guinea hen when she first left the nest with her brood and then, much against her will, penning her up with her babies until they completely feathered out. This was no easy task. First it was necessary to find the nest so cleverly hidden in some remote spot. All of this was a very tricky business necessitating a careful and incessant watch during the early spring. If we had ten guineas and only seven showed up at feeding time, we knew that three of them must be nesting someplace and we must then watch for and then follow these would-be mothers, often a futile job. With some patience and a great deal of luck, we would occasionally find the hidden nest. Having found the nest, a period of careful waiting and watching ensued. We had no way of knowing how long the guinea had been sitting on her nest, so we composed ourselves and waited and watched and waited some more. When the "hatch came off" and the mother started to parade her keets, we were faced with the very real and often painful job of catching her. When we attempted to approach her, she would immediately take wing and fly directly at our heads, at the same time calling for help, so we frequently had the entire flock of angry guineas to contend with. One time we managed to carefully drive a mother guinea through an open barn door, thinking that having her inside, it would be easier to corner her. When we made a quick leap to capture her, she flew into the air straight to the peak of the barn, and turning in flight, she flew out of the topmost window without even waiting to open the window. I can still hear the tinkle of broken glass. Because the window is practically inaccessible, it still has not yet been repaired. Since, however, the mother seldom flew very far from her babies, we were often able to outwit her and capture her along with her brood, and by keeping them in captivity for a few weeks, we would be able to raise them all. Thus by the exercise of wit and patience we were able to slowly increase our flock.

This should be enough on this subject so, in leaving you after this very difficult day at the "office," your Sage of the Roost says:

Since I cannot tell how the truth may be, I must tell this tale as was lived by me.

GEM

BUY IN THE SPRING AND SELL IN THE FALL

Truly, the golden calf doth reward the innocent. You buy in the spring and sell in the fall; now why didn't I think of that?

My dear ones,

Red came into our lives via an auction sale and he was to return that same way six months later. Our first calf, purchased in the spring, was a two-month-old Gurnsey bull, and he was our introduction to the livestock business. We only paid twelve dollars for him, hoping that he would do well and grow strong on the enticing green grasses in our uncut pasture. This he did, probably because we were breaking the law. In Michigan, a bull is not legally allowed to run free, even if the farm is well fenced. Our farm wasn't. As a safety measure, a bull must also be tied at all times and under the complete control of the owner. This is undoubtedly a wise and safe law enacted to protect the public from people like us who wouldn't have the slightest notion of how dangerous a rampaging bull could be. But, we unwittingly went our way and let Red go his way. He prospered and grew fat on the lush grass in our pasture, learning as he grew to come when we called him for his daily ration of grain.

One day in the late fall when the pasture was beginning to fail, we guiltily set about to trick Red, now known as Big Red. He was coaxed into the barnyard and when he bent his head toward a pail of grain which he had by now learned to love too well, we slipped a rope over his unsuspecting head and made a fast loop around his nose. This made a very effective halter. The somewhat battered Chevrolet panel truck which was on loan from my uncle was backed against a nearby berm, a good-sized bank of sod. In spite of his girth, we easily led Big Red into the truck. Having no fear whatever of this gentle animal, we securely tied him, or so we thought. All this was done with the assistance of the Zuverink family—bless them. These wonderful neighbors always seemed ready and willing to lend a most knowledgeable helping hand. They remarked at the docility of Red. Because of the ease with which we had handled this operation, we wondered why we had bothered to even ask for help.

With Big Red safely tied within the truck, I revved the engine and proudly started off for the farmers' auction. Fortunately, my smiling, but somewhat sceptical neighbors who had more years of experience than I had brains, followed. The first ten miles I peacefully floated along on the dreams of success. Then I heard the warning sounds of trouble: a series of crashes. Before I could bring the truck to a stop, Big Red had torn off the brace to which he had been tied, butted open the door with his massive head, jumped into the road where he stood, horns glistening in the sun, shaking his head and snorting. He pawed the gravel with his right front foot, watching us with his very bloodshot eyes. I suddenly had a vision of an arena somewhere in Madrid and I was the matador! But since "fools rush in where angels fear to tread," we calmly backed the truck against a roadside berm and then circled Red, "shishing and shewing and shushing" at him. Red looked at us with disdain, turned around and walked right back into the truck! I slammed the panel door shut and with a borrowed chain I made it as secure as possible. We proceeded to the auction. When we opened the door, Big Red bounded right into the sales pen where with the usual mumble and jumble of "now here, now there," he was sold for one hundred and twenty-five dollars, a neat profit indeed, which was to falsely lead us farther on into the "farm business." We returned untouched and ungored to our River Roost, but were we lucky that day!

GEM

A Little Goat

CHUM'S GOATS

Relating a tragic scene and the ultimate outcome thereof.
A valuable source of food is discovered, the virtue of which
has long been praised in song and story.

My dear ones,

A cat or a dog, or two or three or four of each,
seemed always to be a part of our family, so I can't really
consider them as pets. The first real honest-to-goodness
pet that any of our children had at River Roost was a goat
belonging to Chum. I cannot now remember where that
first goat came from, but I do know that Chum was
extremely fond of it, and when not attempting to ride this
animal, he harnessed it to his little red wagon. We always
had a little red wagon–Cecile wouldn't be without one.
When not thus employed, the goat was usually staked out
to graze. Returning one day from nearby Hamilton where
we had gone to purchase a load of chicken mash, we were
horrified to discover that the chain with which Chum's
goat had been attached to a stake set in the ground was
either just a little bit too long or it was set just a little bit
too close to the fence. Oh, dear, Mr. Goat had jumped
over the garden fence and inadvertently hung himself.
When we discovered the poor animal dangling over the
fence, everyone was, naturally enough, shocked. Chum

burst into anguished sobs accompanied with copious tears. We not only thought that his sorrow would break his heart, but we were afraid that his distress would also break ours. After repeated attempts to calm him, we finally succeeded by promising that we would start out at once to try to find another goat to replace his departed friend. After making inquiries from our neighbors, we were told that on the Town Line Road lived a Mr. Goatman, a tall, one - armed man who kept a fairly large flock of milking goats. Our entire family piled into our car to visit this interesting man who did indeed have quite a few whiskered animals of varying color, size and breed.

The outcome of a long question and answer period with Mr. Goatman was the purchase of not one ordinary goat, but three nannies, one of whom was "fresh" and two who, a short time later, would present us with kids. We somehow managed to get, not only our family, but also our new purchases crowded into the car for a fragrant ride home. After our new charges were somewhat calmed down from their arduous and crowded trip, we offered them some grain. To the one nanny who was "fresh," we gave a particularly large portion. She was placed on a wooden box and while I held a can of grain in front of her, Chum knelt and attempted to milk her. She proved to be a gentle nanny and he was successful in his first try at a new and somewhat jerky occupation.

Goat's milk, when cooled, tasted to us much like

homogenized cow's milk since its cream never rose to the surface. After they became accustomed to the farm, we never used a tether on these goats. They not only followed us everywhere, but more often than not, they rode either on the hood or on the roof of our panel truck. Regardless of the jolting they received during our passage down the hill and over rough ground as we carried drums of water to the range shelters for several thousand growing pullets, they never lost their balance on the smooth surface of our old truck. Their ridiculous antics afforded us all considerable pleasure. With the arrival of the new kids, Chum had three goats to milk which kept him busier, I think, than he had planned.

"By their actions ye shall know them."

By Chum's odor, we knew him!

GEM

THE EGG BUSINESS

A pathetic scene of our entrance into and a discussion of the egg business.

My dear ones,

We came into possession of River Roost in the month of June. We were too late to begin with the earliest stages of this new venture and so we yielded to those fantastic advertisements in the poultry journals and purchased a flock of twenty-week-old starter pullets - six hundred of them, at the going price of $2.25 each. We scrubbed the chicken house with a strong disinfectant and put down clean litter. We bought new feed trays and water fountains. We built new nests and also put in the latest in roosts over a drop board which we almost broke our backs trying to keep clean later for the few hens that used it. Most of our pullets (young leghorns) preferred to roost on the window ledges, the doors, or the roof rafters. When they finally started to lay eggs, they used the floor instead of the nests which we had labored so hard to build. They were a wild bunch. If I thoughtlessly came into their house in a white shirt instead of my usual dull work shirt, they would hit the side of the building shrieking in terror, pile up, and usually smother one or two before I could calm down those most excitable of domesticated fowl.

A leghorn pullet starts to lay eggs at five months and usually does, but not ours. We were assured that they would be in seventy-five percent production at six months, but we didn't see an egg before eight months and their top production never exceeded forty percent. This is not generally true, a fact which we were to learn with later flocks. Leghorns are constantly winning in national egg laying contests; yes, there are such things. Perhaps this first flock wanted to teach us that we were suckers to pay $2.25 for a bird which we couldn't sell for over a dollar when full grown. We finally disposed of the entire flock for the munificent price of twenty cents a pound, averaging about seventy-five cents apiece.

That same fall we bought two hundred Red Rock pullets from one of our neighbors who had raised more than he could comfortably house. The leghorn flock was in the warm chicken house with all new equipment. The Red Rocks were put in a makeshift area on the second floor of our drafty barn with orange crates for nests. Before they were six months old, they were in eighty percent production and when we finally disposed of them for meat, they averaged almost $2.50 each and were well worth every penny.

"The lyf so short, the craft so long to learne,
Thassay so hard, so sharp the conquering."
Chaucer taught me that.   It takes a sage to know that
"Thassay" is "olde" English and means endeavor!

GEM

CAPONS

A discussion of a surgical procedure that is older than the written history of man.

My dear ones,

A capon is, as you probably know and would just as soon not be told about again, is a male, that is to say rooster, chicken that has had, without his permission, his manhood surgically removed at an early age, usually when the bird is between four and six weeks old. The desired result of this 'operation' is to secure a fast-growing, tender-fleshed fowl, which is exactly what happens with a few minor side effects. The main one of these is that the rooster loses his voice to such an extent that his crow becomes a ludicrous chirp. An exceedingly amusing sight it is to see him stretch his wings, fill his lungs with air, cock his head in a masterful manner and attempt to shout out whatever it is that roosters shout about, and then hang his head in shame at his failure. Not only is the flesh of a capon far more tender than that of an ordinary bird, but because he becomes very lazy after his operation, he grows to be a much larger fowl than would ordinarily be the case. So there you have it, a larger and more tender chicken— in short, when roasted, a gastronomically delightful delicacy that anyone would be proud to have grace their dinner table.

Capons, when marketed, proved for us at River Roost a very profitable venture, one that we might well have given far more time and attention, because there was a steady demand for them. An interesting side effect which occurred as a result of turning baby roosters into capons always delighted the children. Picture this: while the incision along his side is healing following the procedure of caponization, air frequently manages to get under the skin and continues to accumulate until the entire skin literally parts from the body of the capon and he puffs up like a full balloon. As he struts around, he seems to almost float, quite unconscious of his comical ailment. In most cases, he will soon resume his normal shape, but sometimes it is necessary to punch a small hole with a needle for the air to escape, sizzling exactly as it does when escaping from a toy balloon. This also gives a new purpose in life for old hat pins!

> Fortune, they say, gives too much to many,
> Yet, she never gave enough to any.
> If Fame and Fortune were in company
> How beautiful would be their harmony.

But if Fame and Fortune are out of tune
Then you take Fame and I'll take the Fortune!

GEM (I know, I hear you groaning!)

MORE CAPONIZING

The gentle art of caponizing....

My dear ones,

With the help of Mr. Barr, the owner of a successful hatchery in Zeeland, we were engaged one day in the tiresome process of caponizing a flock of ten-week-old Rock roosters. With a quick twist of a device, which looked like a loosely strung bow, the feet of a young rooster were imprisoned, and then a small patch of feathers behind the wing and near the backbone was quickly stripped. A small incision was made, and a very small, very sharp hoe-like scalpel was rapidly inserted and as rapidly removed, bringing with it two tiny pink globes, the loss of which created a capon. This procedure was quick, bloodless, and probably painless. The incision healed rapidly with only an occasional side effect, that effect created when air became trapped beneath the skin of the capon. A day or two later he would swell up like a tiny balloon and he would waddle comically around in a most grotesque fashion. The remedy was simple, as you know. Catch the capon and prick his ballooning skin with a needle, collapsing it back to its rightful shape.

Catching, caponizing, releasing these young birds, and then repeating this procedure through some two thousand protesting creatures can become quite a chore. So when Myrna Lee, who had by now blessed us with three years of her life, became a tantalizing nuisance, dodging in and out, frightening the chickens, we finally warned her that if she didn't keep out of the way, she would be treated like the rest of the chickens.

"HUH! You can't caponize me. I don't have any feathers!"

Right you are,
GEM

MORELS, A BLACK CAT, AND A SNAKE

Herein is told a tale of a black cat who bravely protected us from dire danger while we were engaged in the search for the succulent morel.

My dear ones,

Spring fever, that uncontrollable but never fatal illness, more of the mind than of the body, was full upon us all and allowing us to give full reign to a desire to shirk all but the most necessary of duties and to completely abandon ourselves to the sheer luxury of getting up early in order to have more time to loaf! Mushrooms arrive in the spring at about the same time that the fever hits us, so off we must go in search of the elusive morel, the only mushroom that we knew was not poisonous. There are many, many varieties, but this was one that we were sure of and felt quite safe in gathering. The food value of mushrooms is questionable, but their flavor is not—especially when fried in fresh homemade butter. Morels are cone-shaped, sponge-like fungi which appear in the spring following a warm rain and hot muggy days, along with the first mayflowers, violets, adder tongues, jack-in-the-pulpits, Dutchman's breaches and other early wildflowers and plants. Given a warm rain and a muggy day, morels make their appearance overnight, thrusting their way up through the leaf mold, lasting only a few days and then disappearing for another year.

This wild delicacy is often found in old apple orchards, but, as in our case, they are more often found in the wild woodland under a heavy growth of poplar trees. The search for this perfect complement to a steak had become a yearly tradition. However, on our first gathering, Chum, ever the sceptic, watched us very warily at the first meal, eating none until the following day when he found us alive and well; he then decided that it would be safe for him to try! Now, on a bright, beautiful day, our entire family, black cat and black dog included, were on our way to gather mushrooms which we hoped to find in our west woodlot.

Among the profusion of cats that have, from time to time, graced our lives while we lived at River Roost, there were a few with such outstanding characteristics that they will long be remembered for their contributions toward a more interesting life. One of these was Blackie, so named, as you can readily guess, because of her rich, black fur, a blackness of attire, not duplicated until the appearance of Sabaca, many years later. She was also a compulsive mother, and the number of litters which she willy-nilly presented to us was legion. Blackie, like her grandfather, Foxy, would jump upon your shoulder like an unseen bolt from nowhere, landing with a shocking thump with her claws unleashed for proper footing. If you were wearing a light summer shirt, it hurt like billy blue blazes. In the winter when a heavy coat was worn, we accepted this act calmly, without reproof. She would then ride on one's shoulder as long as permitted, which was usually for the duration of the chores.

As we started toward the woods, Blackie walked leisurely at my side, stopping frequently to stretch and yawn in a lazy, carefree manner to such an extent that we all fell under the influence of her lackadaisical manner, a mental condition which was suddenly frightened out of the entire group. We came unsuspectingly upon a water snake, black and shining, but it was foolishly at a distance from the safety of the river which flowed about three hundred feet away. Blackie, with an amazing nonchalance and unconcern, sniffed at the quickly retreating tail of the snake, and then with one graceful bound she arrived at the moving head of the snake, and with one swift motion she culled it with her outstretched claw. A tiny spot of blood appeared at the center of the snake's head where its skull had been pierced. The snake undulated a few times and then became motionless, dead from this one quick thrust of Blackie's paw. The successful warrior paid no heed whatever to this prey from her instinctive attact, but only rested while her warm red tongue pampered her fur. In a moment of idle, senseless curiosity, our black dog Dinah approached to smell of the dead reptile. Immediately the fur on Blackie's neck stood straight up, and then with a warning hiss she again unleashed her claw against this interloper who, recognizing the cat's superior equipment, backed quickly away pretending a false unconcern. This was only a passing incident, a rather mild but shivery interruption to our real purpose: the hunt for that culinary delight—the morel.

With the promise of a munificent reward of a whole nickel to be given to the first child to spot a mushroom, we spread out among the groves of poplars. Nature had given the morel a camouflage which made it very difficult to spot them. Their dark sponge-like appearance blending in with last year's leaves was a decided protection for them. With our eyes glued to the brown, leaf-covered earth so intensely that they began to water, we pressed on in our search. Our efforts, accompanied by shrieks of delight, were copiously rewarded. With a well-nigh perfect growing season, with all those warm, delightful spring smells floating in the air, our mushroom hunt was a great success. Upon returning to the house, we cut the mushrooms in half, carefully washed them, and then with the addition of plenty of homemade butter, we began frying them in a heavy skillet until most of the moisture had been evaporated, leaving only chewy morsels which we heaped upon a tender River Roost steak!

Excuse me now; pass the mushrooms, please.

GEM

NEW CALVES AND OLD VETS

Containing a description of the extraordinary behavior of a grave scientist who must certainly have spent many years delving into ancient tomes the better to advance his medical knowledge and skills.

My dear ones,

River Roost had many acres of splendid pasture as well as many acres not quite so splendid. To take advantage of this fact, we decided one year in our usual naive way to devote a portion of our energies to the raising of calves for "feeders" and perhaps even to finish them off for sale as good quality beef animals. The trick as I saw it was to buy them cheap in the late winter or very early spring, feed them for several weeks in the barn and then, just as soon as the pasture was ready, turn them out to graze. This theory was so full of holes, as I was to discover, that I could have thrown my entire family through any one of them. My hypothesis was based on the hope of a steady three-pound daily increase in weight of young stock properly handled. This was an irresistible vision of easy wealth to be obtained with a minimum of physical effort. All that I had to do was to let them graze to their hearts' content and grow, and grow and grow–, converting fine pasture into finer beef. It certainly should have been profitable. Oh, I tried almost anything to turn an honest penny! My dream was as simple as that. Buy them cheap, graze them during the summer, and then sell them at a fat profit in the fall. A fallacy! I presume that there is always something to be learned by mistakes, but my mistakes were always so expensive. Nevertheless, I had a lot of fun at the auctions buying my calves, bidding against far more experienced buyers, and then toting my purchases home in a decrepit panel truck. In this manner I acquired some twenty-odd calves and everything seemed to be moving smoothly toward my pot of gold.

The calves were housed in the warm barn and each one received individual feeding attention. Everything was fine and I was justly proud. Then the calves developed "scours." Scours in young calves is a serious and often fatal form of diarrhea afflicting calves as well as other young animals. So, now I had a small herd of very sick heifers and bulls. Using what little common sense God gave me, I went to the closest veterinary. He was out on a call, but his wife assured me that he had just the right remedy for the illness in my calves, and that she would have him rush out to our place as soon as he returned. In this she was honest. She did, and he did, and I was happy indeed when he drove into our yard. This veterinary got right down to the business at hand by going immediately to the barn to inspect our ailing animals.

"Scours, umph—yes, scours. I have just the thing for that." The doctor went back to his car and opened the trunk. Here, in several wooden boxes were arrayed many unlabeled bottles of questionable liquids. "Yup, I have just the thing. Hmm, ah yes, this is it." He lifted a large bottle to his lips and tasted the contents and then promptly spit it out. "Nope, not that one. It must be this." He tasted and spit again. "Nope." He lifted another unlabeled bottle. "Ah, yes, this is it, umm. Yup, this is it." And so, after tasting and spitting several times, he returned to the barn and proceeded to douse my already weakened animals. I thanked him and paid him, hoping that his scientific treatment would soon effect a cure, but I was doomed to disappointment. The following morning six of my calves were dead. Seeing my investment fast disappearing, in frustration, I called another veterinary from Holland, who with the use of recently developed drugs not only saved the balance of the animals, but during this same call he made steers out of the baby bulls. You do know how that happens, don't you? It is one of those quick but ouchy little procedures. He also showed us how to get rid of the lice we had purchased along with our calves. His charges were less than those of the "Tasting Doc," who has now reached the age of ninety-seven years, probably by the frequent use of his famous remedies.

So be careful what you're tasting,
GEM

FISHING ON THE KALAMAZOO RIVER

Wherein I unashamedly confess to having lied and led a life full of falsehoods.

My dear ones,

Next to playing cards, my father loved to go fishing, and go fishing he did with the same patience and perseverance of the fish that lay waiting to snap at his bait as it came floating by. He never missed an opportunity to get his line into the water and he never came home empty-handed. He kept a metal boat in our boathouse on the Kalamazoo River and he frequently came to visit us in order to angle for the huge catfish that lurked in that badly polluted water. And there, you see, was the rub. He caught the darn things and he caught them in quantities and he cleaned them most carefully. He very seldom ate fish himself in spite of his incessant angling, but he felt that he was doing us a great favor by giving us those freshly caught and cleaned catfish, which indeed he was, if the fish had come from anywhere else but the Kalamazoo River. At that time the chemical wastes from several large paper mills were fed untreated into the river along with the raw sewage from many villages and cities. Truly, just one taste of those fish was a horrible experience, and so we had to play a game. Suggesting that we would eat them at a later date, we froze and stored them in our freezer until dear Father was absent. Then we would thaw them out and feed them to the dogs, cats, chickens, or pigs who were not quite so discerning. Even with the coming of tough anti-pollution laws and when the river was slowly coming back to life, there was still a problem. You see, the catfish which he caught were BIG ones, and fat with years of browsing and nibbling along the bottom of the river. They were still too strong for our prejudiced appetites. YUCK!

For three years in a row some nitwit came floating down the river, always on the Fourth of July, popping off his twenty-two rifle at anything that he saw. I presume that Dad's metal boat was a perfect target since he completely riddled it each year. This necessitated the drudgery of hauling the boat up a very steep bank and putting it on a trailer to take it to Hamilton to have the holes welded shut to make the boat water tight again and safe for Dad to catch some more giant catfish!

I write this great history all alone,
With many thoughts responsive to your own,
A thousand echoes where your past has flown
Now captured here to give you much renown

With all your honors, you must softly tread,
Or lose those honors while I take the bread!
GEM

Grandpa Bill

BABY DUCKS

Containing heroic matter worthy of your most serious perusal in order that you may thus increase your knowledge on important subjects. Isn't that ducky? This is how we occupied ourselves during our second winter at River Roost.

My dear ones,

Under the hypnotic influence of Bennie, who painted a glorious picture of endless profits, we had raised this particular flock of ducks for breeding purposes, which is to say that these five hundred ducklings were raised for their egg production and the eggs were to be sold to Bennie's Duck Hatchery for incubation. The ducklings had been started in the late summer and as ducks will, they matured rapidly. A Long Island Pekin duckling is full grown and ready for the market anywhere from eight to twelve weeks and at that time our problem was to "rough" these mature ducks through the winter without too large an investment in feed, at the same time maintaining good body weight, so that the ducks would be in a healthy condition to breed and then start to lay continually from early spring until the end of the laying cycle. A properly cared

Cecile Feeding Ducks

for duck will lay approximately one hundred eggs, one
every day until she has completed her mission. Our con-

tract with the hatchery was for ten cents an egg, which at that time was a lot of money and opened a vision of extensive profits. On paper it all looked good, showing a potential gross profit of ten dollars per bird and we would still have the duck left to sell for meat.

Baby ducklings are inherently healthy and are not too difficult to raise, but they did present a few problems not encountered with other domestic fowl. For instance, a duck will drown in a rain storm simply by standing under the eaves of a barn and letting all that lovely water run down his wide-open mouth until he chokes. A duckling, while still in his down and not yet feathered out, tires easily when his down gets water-logged and too heavy for the little fellow, and so he sinks or becomes an easy prey to some hungry fish or turtle.

In late summer and early fall our ducks would daily march in single file like little soldiers down for a swim in the little stream which separated our island from the Kalamazoo River. In this same fashion they always returned night and morning for their allowance of grain. On one particularly and unusually cold Sunday morning when the temperature dropped unseasonably below zero, I was surprised when only a few ducks showed up for their morning meal. Worrying like a father, I walked down in the bitter cold to drive the ducks up so that they could eat and I would thus still have time to drive the family to church. It is hard to conceive how hard I had to work in order to drive normally voracious ducks up to the barn to eat. Having done this and panting from the effort, I finally realized that Mother Nature knows best. The ducks were insistent upon remaining in the water so that, with their constantly flapping wings, they could keep the stream from freezing over. My belated reasoning came to me after I had driven them all up to the barn and fed them. Then they wanted to stay right where they were in the barn, but panting and sweating in the bitter cold, I thought it necessary to drive them back to the stream, only to find a solid sheet of ice covering the water. I returned to the house and procured an ax and for two solid hours I chopped a hole large enough to satisfy the ducks which were far brighter than the chopper. I missed church that morning and caught a cold, but I did learn a lesson. Mother Nature takes care of her own. After this experience we moved the ducks into the barn for the balance of the winter.

In the lower level of the barn, we placed three fifty -gallon barrels with automatic water control attachments. Around these three barrels the ducks gathered in sheer ecstasy drinking and pruning their feathers by throwing water back over their bodies with their shovel bills. I filled these barrels twice each day. Conceive, if you will, what the basement of our barn looked like after three hundred gallons of water had been dumped on the floor in one way or another. Around the edges of the barn away from the muddy mess, we placed planks on edge, behind which we filled about a two-foot space with clean straw, theoretically for nests, but only a few ducks ever realized what this space was for. When they finally started to lay, they dropped their eggs in any handy place for them, but not for us. So, in knee-high boots we harvested our eggs, or attempted to, but with three hundred gallons of water flowing over, around, and through five hundred ducks, you can readily appreciate that we indeed had a problem.

We carefully washed all the eggs before they were sent to the hatchery only to be told that we shouldn't do so because washing might destroy the "hatchability" of the eggs and that the batches from our eggs were poor. We were soon to discover that the real reason that our eggs were not hatching well was not because we washed the eggs, but because the sexers had been in error and that we had too many drakes. One would have thought that these extra drakes would increase the fertility of the eggs rather than the opposite, but such was not the case. For some unknown reason the drakes would systematically pick the weakest hen of the flock and all of them would try to give their amorous attention to this luckless female. While giving her their undeviating love, they would strip the feathers on her back from her head to her tail. This mass courtship would continue until the poor lady duck was dead. In the meantime, her healthier and stronger sisters were laying big, beautiful, and what is more to the financial point, infertile eggs. The reason for this unusual state of affairs baffled everyone, but my speculation would be that the ducks were overcrowded and lacked sufficient green forage.

At the end of the hatching season we sold the ducks for meat and then sat down to figure our net profit. The check from the hatchery paid our feed bill right to the penny so at least we broke even, but we also had their delightful company all winter, and we learned that the reason ducks have shovels for bills is for efficiency, the better to shovel vast quantities of both food and water into their always empty little bodies.

Just before last Christmas nephew Ed Evans and

Toni, his light of love, stopped by the house on their way to pick out a couple of baby ducklings as a joke gift for Toni's father. After proper warning I directed them to the duck hatchery. The following is from a recent note from them.

"Uncle Glenn was right about the ducks. They're cute, but messy. After a couple of weeks of fast growth and mountains of POOP, we weren't so sure we should have gotten them. I have seen them standing there eating and without stopping for a moment, having it come shooting right out the back!"

And now you know all you need to know about ducks.

GEM

CHICKENS

Containing scenes of distress, somewhat whimisical in nature, but nonetheless calling for great fortitude.

My dear ones,

Late that night after we had completed the chores, long after we had shut up the chickens for the night, a precaution against the marauding raccoons, and long after we had hurried the children into their beds, I divested myself of my event-laden clothing and sank onto the edge of the bed with nothing on but my shorts, nodding and dozing, too tired to make that final effort of swinging into bed. Then it happened and I knew instinctively what it was. The loud squawking complaints which came from our pullet house could mean only one thing. When the pullets were small, I had put up a temporary roost, intending to supplant it later when they had grown larger; and now I knew that it had collapsed with the weight that three hundred full-grown rock hens exerted upon it. My own dilatory methods had now come home to roost on my own weary shoulders. A roost that had been built to hold one-pound birds offered no security for five pound, ready-to-lay pullets; and it had broken, accompanied by excited squawks of distress. Still dressed only in my shorts, I eased into an old pair of slippers and grabbing a flashlight, called to Cecile. She promptly wondered if this trip at this time of night was necessary and I patiently explained that it was and that if we didn't get out to the trouble spot at once, the dumb chickens, lacking the least vestige of intelligence, would pile up and smother themselves. The boys, pajama clad and barefoot, offered to help. I accepted their offer, but insisted that they must put something on their feet. One doesn't walk in chicken litter with bare feet since no one had ever been able to housebreak a chicken. After strengthening and repairing the roosts, we carefully, with great forbearing, lifted three hundred pullets from the floor and placed them, one by one, neatly back on the repaired roost, eliminating the danger of suffocation in the terrific heat of that humid July night. We returned to the house and yielded to the supplication for a snack before again retiring. Finally, as I kicked off my slippers and sank again to the edge of the bed, the alarm clock exploded, and I believe that I did too!

And this Sage wonders if ye have heard of the patience of Job?

GEM

COOKED CHEESE

Wherein we turn our hands to the manufacturing of certain table delicacies by churning from the mysterious recipes of ages-old dairies.

My dear ones,

With two gentle black Jersey cows overflowing with rich milk, far more than a family of six could consume, it was inevitable that we search out uses for our surplus, and in a small way become ingenious manufacturers of sorts, with the end product for our own use only and for our friends and relatives, of course, who were legion. We made our own butter and wonderful ice cream as well as dish after heaping dish of cottage cheese. It was this surplus of cottage cheese that led us faltering along into the production of "cooked cheese." This was a smooth, spreadable cheese, pale in color with an ivory tint, having a mild, but delicate, nutty taste which was complemented by the old-world taste of caraway seeds mixed into the cheese during its final stage of cooking. It was this process of cooking whereby it earned its appropriate name.

"Smelling to high heavens" was an expression expressly developed for this task. Actually, the entire process stunk! But more so while it matured. The cottage cheese was spread out in thin layers in large baking pans and allowed to cure slowly in a constant eighty-degree temperature, either in the summer's sunny rays or in an open but heat-controlled oven. At this temperature the lumps of cottage cheese would gradually melt into a viscous, smelly mess. When all the curds had softened, this sticky, syrupy product was scraped into a heavy skillet and cooked, with constant stirring until it became a creamy textured cheese. After the addition of the caraway seeds and a light salting, it was poured into large-mouth jars to cool and thicken, becoming finally a very edible, high-protein food almost too mild for the average taste. But it was a cheese that Cecile dearly loved and which we imported from Wisconsin when we no longer made our own. One of our local markets has now begun to stock this item, making Cecile very happy, indeed.

What were once vices are now manners, and that which was once slop is now a luxurious tidbit for the fastidious gourmet.

A timely interjection by the Sage of River Roost, don't you think?

GEM

GEORGE Z. AND CHEWING TOBACCO

A short bit about George and sundry other observations.

My dear ones,

George Zuverink, a short, thin, slightly hump-backed man with loose, rope-like muscles of surprising strength, was our closest neighbor who would, it seemed, rather come to our place to help us, than work on his own farm. He had little use for the new farm methods, preferring to till the soil behind a team of very large but old horses. He even preferred to sow seed by hand; and it was no uncommon sight to see him walking up and down a long field wearing a canvas sack and flicking his fingers in a half-moon circle, casting the seed in a regular pattern. During the hot summer days he would be walking through row on row of field corn laboriously hoeing while other farmers were cultivating with their tractors. He would yearly plant a garden several times the size needed by his small family, cultivate it by hand and then give away to his friends most of the harvest. He had one time made a trip to visit relatives in northern Indiana, the one and only time he had ever been away from home, and the only time that he had been out of the state. So I, along with my children, took him to the Museum of Science and Industry in Chicago. Thereafter he never ceased telling about that tremendous adventure. George also chewed tobacco. Eight Brothers, I believe, and strong it was, but he never was seen to spit. Instead, he swallowed the yellow juices and bragged about his ability to do so. The concentrated nicotine (I used it on chicken roosts to ward off mites) never seemed to faze or upset his cast-iron stomach. A lovable, ever helpful man, never voicing a complaint, George was our good neighbor—bless him!

When I was a boy, chewing tobacco was a very common thing and more men than not had a telltale streak of yellow running from lips to jaw. My father smoked incessantly, but we were spared the dirty chore of cleaning and polishing the brass spittoons which adorned most parlors—he never chewed. However, we had a neighbor who did and when he came in from the fields where he had been working, he deposited his "chew" on the top of a fence post. After a few days of drying in the sun, this same chew was crammed into a pipe and smoked. Our neighbor was a saving man!

Smoked or chewed, beware the nasty tobacco weed.

GEM

A BAT ON THE FOURTH OF JULY

Containing an adventure shared by that amiable lady, Aunt Selma, Cecile's youngest sister, with other members of the family and this truthful historian. While it may seem to have supernatural overtones, or at least to have come from the pages of some science fiction tale, it really happened on one early holiday morning.

My dear ones,

This particular Fourth of July was to be a weekend family "get-together." It opened, as our Fourths usually did, with dawn's early light eruption of a series of noisy bangs caused by the fire crackers which the boys were throwing out of their upstairs bedroom window, much to the dismay of the two dogs, Dewey and Dinah. It frightened poor Dinah, our little black cocker spaniel, so out of her wits that at the first opportunity she dashed down into the basement to find security in a dark quiet corner. There she remained, in spite of our pleadings, for the entire day, not daring to venture out from her safe corner to again be plagued by those infernal pops and bangs.

There was a dark shadow against the white curtain of the upstairs bathroom; like some uncanny omen, there clung a bat. The appearance in our home of this strange creature was not only unusual and unexpected, but it was in a physical sense a shock which sent shivers in waves over my body as ghoulish bat stories rushed through my mind. It may have been Teddy who made the discovery, but it was with Aunt Selma's shriek, informing me of her awareness of this soft reddish bit of mammalian wonder, that the understanding came to me that something must be done immediately to capture this queer mouse-like creature. I had to either expel it from the house or preserve it for an examination by the smaller children before freeing it into the wild. To view a live bat would be a new and exciting experience for them as it now was for us. When Aunt Selma sounded the alarm again with her second yelp, I moved quickly! With a crumpled bath towel, wary of being bitten, my mind full of long-toothed vampire stories, I quickly covered the bat; and with my fingers I worked the toweling completely around the body to prevent an escape before moving it. Carrying it in triumph to the kitchen, we deposited it into our daughter Kay's abandoned parakeet cage which Myrna Lee had by this time resurrected from the basement. Still loosely wrapped in the towel, the tiny insect-eating, winged animal was carefully released inside the safety of the closely woven wire frame. Then, as it extricated itself from the towel, we watched in amazement and incredulous disbelief as it easily and quickly, with a sideways motion, slipped between the wires and escaped from the cage.   This was an unbelievable occurence in view of the size of this nocturnal flying mammal; small as it was, it seemed quite impossible for a maneuver of this nature to occur.   But now the bat was swooping in winged flight around the kitchen and we were all shrieking at each dive-bomb approach to our heads.   It stopped occasionally to cling to the ceiling molding for a rest, and then it quickly continued its frightened rush when we approached too close to it.   With a ludicrous attempt to keep hair and heads protected, in an abiding belief in all those legendary stories about how bats love to get into one's hair, Aunt Selma had her newspaper and I had my towel.   It is questionable who was more frightened, the fleeing bat or the pursuing humans.   With a final flying circle around the kitchen, the bat flitted through the door and up the stairwell into our bedroom.   The only sound that we heard was the short shrill shrieks as it flew by us on its leathern wings.   With an urgency growing from a desire not to admit defeat from this tiny timid animal, we made all haste in pursuit.   The bat had come to rest, hanging by means of the claws of its hind feet, on our

bedroom curtain. Small, specialized, pointed ears standing peculiarly upright, or rather downward, topped its
head, listening perhaps, while it rested. It seemed to stare
at us with tiny, beady, black eyes. In this position, for the
first time, we were able to see the thin folds of almost
transparent skin which stretched between the clawless
front fingers and extended to the ankles of the rear feet,
enveloping the tail. It was equipped with a claw on its
thumb. Now, in the calmness which finally enveloped us,
we realized that this could not be a vampire with long-
pointed teeth, the better to puncture our skin in search of
a supply of blood (oh, I do read too much!); but rather
indeed, it was only one of nature's marvels whose particular mission in life was, with a nervous system similar to
radar and an almost supernatural touch, to capture insects
and assist us in keeping the insect population under control. Curious as we might be, we had no right to take away
a freedom which belongs to all creatures. After much discussion on the possibilities of our bat being a carrier of
rabies, we caught it again in the towel and our brave Teddy
carried it down to the barn where he released it. In doing
this, we knew full well that we were laying ourselves open
to charges that we were acting too hastily before others
had had an opportunity to view this creature which

whirred about under cover of darkness. But we also knew that we had set free one of nature's best mosquito eaters.

One of the latest "fads" is to paint the interior of dried milkweed pods in brilliant colors for use as Christmas tree decorations. Cecile bought one of these the following December and has it hanging on our bedroom curtain. In the deep of the night when the moonlight flows through our window, this darkened figure stands out against the curtain exactly as did the bat that Fourth of July; and when I awaken in the middle of the night as I usually do, it gives me again and again a small shiver.

I remain your pensive Sage of River Roost.

GEM

AUNT HAZEL AND A SUMMER DAY

A short time ago Aunt Hazel wrote to question me as to why I had failed to write about a certain subject. In my answer to her letter, I had to admit that I had no recollection whatever about this particular incident and I wondered if she wouldn't refresh my memory, or better yet, write about this bit of history in detail, and so she did. The following is Aunt Hazel's answer, bless her delightfully agreeable heart and memory. A good one it is too!

Dear Glenn,

It was a very hot summer weekend and while you folks were all buzzing off to Grand Rapids to the Lutheran church, we decided to go to mass at the Catholic church in Allegan on that Sunday morning. This particular weekend Tyke, the nickname for Myrna Lee given to her by her dear father and used only when she was a very little girl, was getting the princely price of one cent for five dead flies, paid by her devoted and generous papa! As a result she was continually dragging a chair around to swat the flies on the ceiling. They were really plentiful—the flies, I mean. To get back to Sunday morning, Uncle Johnny and I got back from mass, got out of our Sunday clothes and into something cooler. As "per orders from head-quarters" (that is to say, Cecile) we set the table, pared potatoes, fed the chickens and "slopped" the hogs. Then we mixed ourselves a tall cold glass of you know what!

When you folks got home from church, Glenn went down to the barn to see if the city dudes had carried out all the instructions. One of the pigs had tried to dig his way out of the pen and was strangling, so Glenn slit his throat and hung him in a tree so the meat would drain and could be used. In the meantime somebody had inadvertently left the gate open so all the pigs got out and they were running around the field. Cecile and Glenn were determined to get the pigs back into the pen and with the dubious help of the children, the dogs, and those two city folks, we all ran around like maniacs chasing those little pigs. Eventually the pigs were corralled, and although the kids reveled in it, Cecile's, Glenn's and Johnny's faces were as red as beets and I knew that mine must also be. Why someone didn't get sunstroke or heat prostration was due to the goodness of the Lord. So back to the house and the continued cooking of Sunday dinner. All the flies that Tyke had neglected to kill had issued a clarion call for their relatives and literally thousands showed up, lured by the smell of the draining pig. While Cecile went on with frying the chicken for dinner, Tyke was busy counting dead flies. When the smell of the frying chicken drifted outside, the flies decided that the chicken was a better deal than the pig. As a result, every time anyone went in or out the back screen door, scores of flies entered the house.

Cecile ordered the spray can out and Tyke was bewailing the fact that her mother was taking away her money-making venture. So every time the can of spray was used, the chicken and the table were covered. The afternoon wore on with intermittent cries of "COVER THE CHICKEN!" The tiny dead soldiers were swept up with Tyke trying to garner a few extra dead flies for her pile with the hope of being paid a little more by her father. How young and trusting she was!

I think the meat from the pig was packaged and put into the freezer by nightfall. I don't remember playing pinochle that night; we were just too tired out. It may have been a hectic day, but still a pleasant one of many at River Roost. Those city folk, who most always arrived unexpectedly, were sure of their welcome which continues to this day.

Love to you all,
Aunt Hazel

KAY'S TEARFUL RIDE

A 1949 drama of considerable importance which points to a moral which is simply this: Bathe and dress before accepting a ride! This moving vehicle episode stars that winsome four-year-old Kay and co-stars her capable eleven-year-old brother, Chum. Also, co-starring is that six-year-old, disappointed, "Let me ride!" pensively passive brother Teddy, cast in the minor role of a bystander; and not to forget, also co-starring is that eleven-month-old newcomer, the inimitable, Teeny, Tiny Tykie (Myrna Lee to you).

My dear ones,

With her arms around Chum's middle, Kay perched precariously on the rear fender of a bicycle, trying to balance herself with her heels resting loosely on the axle while they circled the house with gay and happy peals of laughter. Her delicate balance was suddenly destroyed when the bicycle swerved as it struck a stone; and it was then that Kay's left heel slipped off the axle and was caught in the driving gears! What had been joyful laughter now became moans and groans accompanied by copious tears. Replying to her shrieks of pain, Mother and I rushed to

Kay's rescue.

"Keep the wound clean! Soak it in a warm boric acid solution," was my advice. However, when that terribly mangled heel was tenderly washed in warm water, we realized that our poor efforts at first-aid would not be enough. We immediately carried her to the car; and after a wild and fretful ride to Holland we rushed Kay, followed by three frightened urchins with dirty, tear-streaked faces and ragged clothes, into the emergency entrance of the hospital.

Mother, moaning under her breath about the external condition of her brood, was relieved, as were we all, when under the direction of our doctor the excruciatingly painful wound in Kay's heel was properly cleaned, stitched, and bandaged. All sobbing subsided when the promise of a special treat was made. Our nondescript family headed for a dairy store, famous for its multi-flavored double-and triple-decker ice cream cones.

"Little Tykie is much too young to handle a cone by herself," I declared. "She will just mess up everything and everybody."

"Oh, no," replied Mother. "This will be her very first ice cream cone; let her have her own."

So, we did, and naturally, as have thousands of

children before her, she promptly bit off the bottom of the cone, which, in the July heat, began at once to run and drip. We were thus, as I had predicted—with my usual keen vision and foresight!—in addition to our already soiled condition (filthy is the proper word for it) made very messy indeed.

Sticky, but relieved, we again came home to River Roost where Kay was to begin her many weeks of painful limping. Her heel, healed these many years, still carries an angry-looking scar.

So consider then that possibility of always being properly dressed for an emergency. Why, the world would stand still and nothing would ever happen!

And thus end Acts 1,2, and 3 of a play by your Sage of River Roost!

GEM

A BLOW SNAKE !

Disclosing a strange and awesome encounter with one of nature's interesting and helpful creatures who is often wrongly molested.

My dear ones,

Perhaps because we raised chickens, we very seldom saw many snakes on our farm. Chickens are intrigued with anything that wriggles, and if a snake should unsuspectingly wander into a chicken yard, the entire flock will descend upon it immediately and begin to furiously peck at it until even a bare skeleton is hardly visible. It seemed at least once each spring, however, that we would encounter near one of our large, ancient and hollow oak trees, a "blow snake." I must confess to my ignorance of the Latin name which a scientist might use to designate this peculiar and harmless fellow, but to my untrained mind he was then and he still is a "blow snake," a name that I have always felt was most apt. When frightened, this snake forms a coil, raises and hoods his head exactly like a cobra. He will then start to hiss with a peculiar blowing sound and this noise issuing from his rather frightening hooded head will usually scare anybody in his path. Like some humans, he is all "front." His hiss and his hood are sheer bluff and if he doesn't succeed in frightening you, he will quickly wriggle away.

Coming up from the garden one spring day, we found a "blow snake" blocking our path. He was momentarily incapable of putting up his usual bluff because he had just started to eat. It is most amazing how such a small head can become so apparently disjointed and enlarged, for this snake was engaged in the attempt of swallowing a very large bull frog. We surrounded him and watched in sheer fascination with occasional calls to the house to enlarge our audience. The dogs came barking and the children came shouting. The noise was too much and the poor snake gave up in what must have been disgust. To our surprise and amazement he suddenly regurgitated the badly mauled frog and quickly disappeared into the tall grass, as believe it or not, also did the frog.

Oh, yes, I remember it well!

GEM

Blow Snake

PORKY COMES TO THE ROOST

My dear ones,

Aunt Hazel has done it again! From the depths of her amazing memory she has come up with another pig story which goes like this (her words): Late one Friday afternoon those unexpected but always welcomed Feils from Chicago popped in again at the Roost. After one of Cecile's delicious chicken and dumpling dinners, Glenn announced that they were going shopping for a pig. Now, dear me, I am a professional at food shopping and have even been known to drop in and buy a dress or a piece of furniture, but a pig? What more delightful way is there to spend a fall evening with good friends:

We piled into two cars and took off, and shortly thereafter the McNitts had acquired a new member of River Roost. It was decided that he would ride home in the trunk of the old Nash. The pig couldn't be persuaded to lie down, so the trunk door was tied over him, while he was standing, in order that he might get some air, but he couldn't get loose. Meanwhile, "Porky" was filling the air with his squeals.

Glenn decided that he and Uncle Johnny would take the long way home and Cecile should take the short cut and we'd all have a chance to chat. It may have been a short cut, but it was sure a bumpy one. Basically, it was a "two tracks in the sand" kind of road with several soft spots along the way so the car would touch bottom every now and then, jolting everyone into saying "WOW! That was a pretty good one!" Every time we hit a bump in the road, the pig would squeal a notch higher. When he was quiet, we all figured that maybe he was unconscious or the rope was broken and that he had jumped out and run away in the woods. Out we'd all pile, Cecile leading the charge with her big flashlight. When the pig, who was only taking a breather, saw that big "white eye" and those shining pairs of little eyes, he let us know in loud tones what he thought of this whole expedition. He wasn't very happy but at least he was still there. Back into the car we would pile. But the next time that the pig was quiet and we thought of chasing an escaped pig through the darkness, we'd get out of the car in a hurry again.

Meanwhile, the "two gentlemen from Verona" were tooling along and chatting away, with nary a care in the world. Cecile was trying to slow down and take the bumps easy, but we'd hear that animal's head get clunked again and again and we'd wince in sympathy. By some quirk of childish fancy the children's sympathy was all for the pig. While Cecile tried to stay in the ruts of this muddy road, she also had to listen to the incessant chant from the back seat. "Mother-r-r, you are killing that pig!" Their tone implied that if we arrived home with a dead pig, Cecile and

105

I could swing from that big tree outside the library window and not sitting in the swing either!

At long last, we could see the lights of River Roost at the end of the road. Believe it or not, the two gentlemen were waiting, and one of them inquired, "What took you so long?" Cecile, being too much of a lady, had no reply whatsoever, and so it was that the Mc Nitt pig came home to "Roost."

The eight of us (that would be Glenn and Cecile, Chummy, Ted, Kay, Myrna Lee, and Uncle Johnny and Aunt Hazel) were the same ones who had chased those little pigs on a Sunday afternoon, and this may have been the start of that particular brood. If so, Patricia Porky or Peter Pig (was it a boy or girl pig? I can't remember!) had his or her porcine revenge for that ignoble ride!

With love to you all,
Aunt Hazel

CANADA GEESE

A haze on the far horizon
An infinite tender sky,
The ripe, rich tint of the cornfield
And the Wild Geese sailing high;
And all over upland and lowland
The charm of the goldenrod.
Some of us call it autumn
And others call it God.

William Herbert Carruth

My dear ones,

All along the Kalamazoo River from the Allegan Dam to Saugatuck on Lake Michigan's beautiful, sandy beaches wild Canada Geese come in huge migrating flocks with a considerable number of them remaining all winter. Near what is known as the "High Banks" is the famous Todd Farm, now a state-owned, conservation department-operated feeding station and sanctuary for Canada Geese. Here, large fields of corn are planted yearly and in the fall and early winter it is harvested by the wild geese, a memorable sight which hundreds of people would come to

107

watch in wonder and amazement. For many miles the Kalamazoo River, each fall and spring, is literally alive with this beautiful game bird. When the heavy snows come, the high water overflows the banks in secluded river bottoms. The geese would keep the water there from freezing by constant agitation and swimming in this shallow water, and they would feed on the grasses growing a few inches beneath the surface, and at the same time, unfortunately, offer an easy target for the poacher.

Wild geese would start arriving in the fall, usually in October at about the same time when the legal bird hunting season opened. Just as frequently, however, they arrived after the season had closed much to the bitter disappointment of the hunter who had purchased his "Duck and Goose Stamp." Geese migrate by a natural weather instinct and not by arbitrary human dates. When the geese arrived on time all hunters were happy; but when they were late, loud were the complaints and cries of irritation against a law which would take a man's money for a hunting license when there was no game available until after the season was over. To the poachers, and they were many, open seasons meant little or nothing. They hunted when the birds came.

The sight of a large flock of geese in flight with

their quaint honking has never lost its thrilling appeal, particularly so on a bright, balmy spring day when they are flying so low that you can see their coloring and even hear their wings sizzling in rapid motion. Of course, they are noisy too, constantly honking with their shrill, incomparable voices. On dark and gloomy days they seem to fly higher and they are scarcely visible, but they are always audible. In the spring they are in constant flight all during the day, but particularly more so in the early morning and late afternoon. It is interesting to watch a lone scout fly out, a lonesome figure against the bright sky, returning shortly, apparently to tell his fellow geese that all is safe and well. A large flock is then in immediate flight, perhaps to raid some farmer's unguarded field of grain to pick up the lost kernels from the fall harvest. Whenever a lone goose would be seen, you would always know that shortly a large flock would appear, flying in their near perfect V formation. Suddenly, usually sometime in April, those wild beauties would be gone, flying farther north to their breeding and nesting grounds, no longer to be seen until their return in the fall.

Your Sage remains a friend to the "Wild Geese,"

GEM

FUNERAL ARRANGEMENTS

Relating a community custom entirely new and strange to us.

My dear ones,

A short time after we had moved to River Roost, while I was milking in the basement of the barn, Ed Lenart called on me to inform me that Mrs. George Zuverink had passed away. While informing me of this sad event, he told me that all of the neighbors would meet at the house of the deceased at nine-thirty that evening in order to make arrangements for the funeral. This type of thing, I had always thought, was a matter only for the intimate family to take care of, but I was now to learn that even in the most unhappy of human affairs, our little community had its own strict ritual to follow; and so it was, that at nine-thirty the neighbors met together with the undertaker and the minister. Not knowing better, it seemed quite natural for Cecile to accompany me, only to discover that on these occasions and at most other formal gatherings, only the men met to conduct whatever arrangements were necessary. Consequently, Cecile was the only woman present. However, her presence was not too embarrassing since Bernice, the daughter, certainly needed a woman's attention during the first shock of her grief.

At this meeting, all the details for the funeral were arranged by the men, or I should say the male neighbors. Who would do this? Who would do that? Who would notify certain relatives? Who would notify the friends? The neighbors did all of this and considerably more.

Later, of course, the women took over, bringing in more than an ample supply of food of almost every description from meat dishes to delicate pastries, thus eliminating completely for any member of the deceased's family the necessity to cook for the three days prior to the funeral. After the final services, the family, friends, and neighbors solemnly met again where the inevitable "lap"lunch was served.

After all this disquieting, but interesting information, your tired old Sage suggests to you that Cecile will be quite unnerved when she comes home this evening. Sabaca has just tipped over the Valentine bouquet which adorned our dining room table. Oops!

Hoo boy! Offer a silent petition for
GEM

UNCLE AL AND THE SHEEP SHOOT

Where is the shepherd who will protect the sheep from the fox who would snatch them up?

My dear ones,

After two sad years of losses from killer dogs harassing and mortally injuring our sheep, we have through natural increase built our flock up to twenty-one animals. However, our last year's crop of lambs seemed to run mostly to bucks. As you know, we always dock the tails of the newborn ewes and for purposes of identification allow the bucks to retain their long tails. We did accidentally miss one of the ewes and allowed her tail to grow. Uncle Al, who has a proprietary interest in our flock, decided it would be a "fun game" to butcher, cut up, and package for freezing our excess bucks and that he, with Aunt Ruth's help, could easily do this without any extra help. Knowing what this job consisted of, however, I took a few days off from the road and with knife, saw, and cleaver, lent a hand. Uncle Al butchered and skinned, Aunt Ruth packed, and I did the cutting into the various pieces of roasts and chops. Now, this is the way it went. First, we very carefully explained to Uncle Al that no ewes were to be killed and that the old buck (easily distinguished by his large size and physical equipment) should also be spared. Only this year's crop of young buck lambs (there were four of them) were to be slaughtered. So, with block and tackle, a rifle and the tractor, Uncle Al started on his hunting expedition. His first success, quite properly, was a nice tender young buck. His second was the long tailed ewe we had missed docking the previous year. His third (ah, you have guessed it!) was, of course, the old buck. You see this really was a game to Uncle Al. He did not keep the sheep in the barn behind closed doors. No, he went hunting! Astride his valiant steed (an old but surprisingly good and dependable tractor he had bought for a "song" from Camp Concordia) which he had brought out here to the farm, he rode down to the pasture to do his shooting. He would say, "I shot this one from at least a hundred yards," or, "I got this one from two hundred feet—a dead center shot in the neck." Then he would hook his "kill" behind the tractor and drag the animal up to the huge oak tree in the yard (the old tree where there had always been a swing for the children), and with block and tackle he would raise the animal for skinning. He was having a "ball." Like Uncle Remus' Tar Baby, I didn't say anything, but I sure wondered how size and physical attributes could so easily be missed, and unlike Brer Fox, I didn't "lay low," but quickly checked in our library for the gestation period of sheep, to happily find that it was from 145 to 152 days. So, we are indeed fortunate, and in all probability our ewes have already been bred. We needed a new buck anyway to prevent inbreeding. However, with our freezer already overflowing, we still have three more young lamb bucks to slaughter. Uncle Al will go hunting again in December, when he returns from his annual "wild deer" trip up north.

Please take a few packages of lamb chops out of the freezer when you go home today, won't you?

GEM

APPLES AND APPLESAUCE

Containing a series of strange incidents which first led to a deception which lay heavily upon my soul, but after a great deal of advice and considerable labor on the part of interested relatives my deception was exposed and the truth resulted in a very famous recipe.

My dear ones,

Far back in the dim past, someone had planted four fruit trees on our farm; these were two unnamed apple and two unnamed pear trees. For years, long before we arrived at River Roost, these trees had been so badly neglected that their trunks were twisted out of shape. They resembled something that only a tortured mind could imagine. The fruit from these trees, if there was any fruit at all, was small, pithy, ill-shaped and riddled with worm holes. In a very good year, we sometimes were able to can a half dozen quarts of pears and perhaps, when we were able to undergo the wasteful, time-consuming labor, an equal number of quarts of applesauce.

When my father was recuperating from surgery, clad only in his pajamas, a bathrobe, slippers and a straw hat, he took long walks every day and he would return from this exercise triumphantly bearing a pail full of misbegotten and forlorn apples which he expected us to convert into applesauce. I made a brave pretense of going through the motions of preparing this delicacy of which he was inordinately fond, but the small quantities of sauce which resulted from an enormous amount of labor while processing these apples forced me into using many subterfuges to evade this work. The apples which he harvested ultimately found their way to the barn where I fed them to the sheep who were not quite as discerning as I had come to be, since the thought of biting into a half a worm was equal to biting into a whole worm!

Uncle Al decided that something must be done about these trees, so one year, acting on the advice of my cousin who operated a large and successful fruit farm, he carefully pruned and sprayed and sprayed and pruned our trees. Then we waited expectantly. The results were almost unbelievable. In the fall following Uncle Al's tree surgery his patients were loaded with large, smooth-skinned, deliciously juicy fruit. The apples, which looked like a cross between a Russet and a yellow delicious, were particularly good, having a delicate, wine flavor which defied comparison. This was the year when we finally gloried in making an applesauce of which we could be proud. Nor was it necessary to sneak these apples off to the sheep.

In making sauce, I would quarter the apples,

remove the core, pare, slice into bite-size pieces and after adding the proper amount of sugar and water, boil them until they were tender. Now, Uncle Leonard, who was extremely fond of fruit (he could, and he often did, eat a quart of peaches at a sitting), explained to me that while my sliced applesauce looked beautiful, I was going through many unnecessary steps to make my sauce, and that it would be much faster and easier to cook the whole apple and then run the cooked fruit through a food mill, which would produce, with a minimum of effort, a smooth and tangy product. His speeded-up recipe, told in his own words, follows:

Having several bushels of apples in the basement and being alone at home, I thought it was a good time to make some applesauce. I started by filling the largest pot I could find with raw apples and water, and set it to boil. As the apples began to soften, I brought out the food mill and filled it with the hot, soppy apples and merrily began cranking away, forcing the sauce through the sieve into another large pot set underneath. This bottom pot would fill up, so I got another pot to fill with my finished prod-uct. I also needed another pot so I could scrape the pulp residue into it. So, there I was grinding away, with four pots full of hot applesauce on the narrow table near the kitchen door. My beagle hound, who always did her sleeping under this table, began to look a bit nervous at this point. All would have been well, but unnoticed by me the small table had been vibrating as I cranked and suddenly a pot full of fresh applesauce went off the end of the table, landed on its edge, whiplashed the pot which then slapped applesauce into my face, splashed up three walls, slid down the kitchen door and then oozed all over the floor. My little hound suddenly decided to get out of there, so standing in applesauce up to my ankles I reached over and opened the door. There stood Carol, my daughter, just home from school. She had a look of startled wonderment on her face. The beagle, not caring much about walking through hot applesauce, hesitated a bit; so to give her moral support, I slid her through the applesauce and out the door with my foot, and I'm afraid that I cursed a wee bit while doing so. "What is going on here?" asked Carol incredulously. "Can't you see that I am making applesauce?" I said.

Uncle Leonard's speeded-up applesauce recipe sounds to me like it has a few things to work out yet, so I'll stick to my way and let him stick to his.
Have you had some good homemade applesauce lately?

GEM

NEW YEAR'S EVE

Containing matters pertinent and impertinent which are
here put together in order to form a composite picture of
extraordinary behavior which often would happen during
the course of one evening's celebration.

My dear ones,

It began early in our occupancy of River Roost and
slowly, as the years merged one into the other, an all-night
New Year's party became a traditional event to which we
all looked forward. Now as we approach another party in
our old/new home and I look backward, it seems almost
inconceivable that we were ever able to arrange sleeping
accommodations for as many people as we packed into all
available niches and corners. To the best of my recollection, it went something like this: the double bed in the
guest room, two; the twin bed in the same room, one, but
more often two; two in the boys' room; two in our room;
two comfortably in the twin beds in the girls' room, but
more often than not, two each; two each on the red davenports in the library; one each on the other two davenports in the living room; six in sleeping bags on the floor
under the grand piano or near it at the far end of the liv-

ing room; four to six more on the floor in the library, and four to six more (usually the little children) in sleeping bags in the dining room, under the table, of course. All this totals somewhere between twenty-six and thirty-six people attempting to sleep amidst giggling whispers, raucous snores, and the pleasant crackling sound of someone stoking the fire in the fireplace. Add to this total ten to fifteen more who came for the evening, but went home, Cinderella fashion, shortly after the clock struck twelve.

A potluck buffet lunch was always available on the overladen dining room table with a huge, thirty-cup coffee urn on a little square antique table a few feet away. The urn was surrounded by additional snacks and dirty coffee cups which some good soul was trying to keep abreast of by washing them along with the fast-emptying glasses from the buffet, where bottles of liquor and mixes of almost any description appeared next to a bowl of eggnog. Along with a main dish, everyone also brought their own bottle which, darn it, they also took home. Ah yes, the many delicious dishes which appeared from year to year on our table, and which, I suppose, I should describe in detail; but rather than slight some person by overemphasizing the delights of their particular dish, allow me instead to introduce you to a certain Aunt Minnie, who always took first place and the prize for her potato salad at the county fair and at all bazaars and church suppers.

But alas, poor Minnie cheated,
Her opponents were by guile defeated,
For across the town in Schmidt's arcade
She bought her salad ready made!

This I threw in because it also describes my famous almond bark which I have been sending out to a favored few who have been overwhelming me with their compliments when all that I did was to melt chunks of white chocolate in the double boiler, to which I added the almonds. (I did so crack the almonds!) No, I shan't attempt to describe the variety of all those delicious dishes offered on New Year's Eve, but rather, I will leave to your own fertile memory to recall them. I might, however, remind you of the Limburger cheese that Uncle Ed brought and the Beer Casse furnished by Walter and left over from Christmas. The consumption of these two cheeses, for reasons which I could never understand, seemed to be the greatest of jokes—a humor as strong and unsavory as the breath of the consumer. Concoctions which defy the most vivid imagination and at the same time challenge the strongest cast-iron stomach were tossed together at the sideboard. Still, in spite of the number of

121

attractive shiny bottles offered there, an unusual modera-
tion always prevailed.

Pinochle, Terry's special forte, was of all the many
games played the most popular and it evolved into a yearly tournament watched over and guided by the scorekeep-
ing Terry, who posted the names of the winners on a fancy
shield which he had made for that purpose and which
yielded him an enormous amount of pleasure since his
name always appeared at the top. Terry took his pinochle
seriously!

The temperature had continued to drop on this
early, cold New Year's morning and tiny streamers of frost
appeared on the telephone lines, hanging from the tree
branches and from the bushes. Everywhere, everything
shimmered with a diamond-like brilliance and the silence
of a fifteen-below-zero morning was only occasionally broken by the loud snap of a tree's sap exploding when trying
to escape as it expanded too   rapidly from the intense
cold. A few of our guests decided it was time to leave. It
was then that they discovered that the only car that would
start in the terrific cold was the decrepit '52 Buick, which
had passed from family to family as that 'extra' car and,
regardless of who bought it, it always seemed to sell again
and again for $50.00. It was with the aid of this car (it

had finally descended to us) that the shiny new models were finally started.

On one clear, cold New Year's Eve when the full moon lighted our fields with a glimmering glory of white radiance and your breath froze into misty wisps of tiny clouds which floated lazily in the below-zero air, all the young folk decided, at three o'clock in the morning, to go tobogganing. They actually claimed that they couldn't sleep in a house with so much snoring going on. So with whoops of exuberant joy reverberating through the house, they bundled on their wraps and escaped to our rolling meadow to begin their wintry sport, which lasted until almost five o'clock, reawakening everyone else with their clattering noise when they returned to make BREAK-FAST! Oh well, from my slumber I felt jolted awake as though a snarling dog had bitten me; but once my eyes were open, their kitchen racket didn't seem to really matter.

So with breakfast came New Year's morning.

GEM

NEW YEAR'S MORNING

On each festive occasion there was always something of interest to capture and hold attention.

My dear ones,

Poor Uncle Leonard! His idea of the proper way to start out New Year's Day was to go rabbit hunting in the forest, usually starting out in the wee small hours of a new dawn. One such hunting trip started out on, perhaps, the most miserable, intensely cold New Year's morning that ever ushered in a new year. With a bitter, icy, below-zero wind blowing sharp, frozen particles of snow in swirling clouds, making visibility quite impossible, he met only refusals when he attempted to get someone to go with him. As a more intelligent person than I once said, "Tain't fit for man nor beast" in describing a morning of like nature, but there was no denying Uncle Leonard his hunting when a-hunting he would go. His unfortunate hound, Bessie, had been stationed in the hall where she threatened to bite anyone who foolishly attempted to pass her. Bundled up for the fierce storm which was unrelentingly raging outside, Uncle Leonard unleashed Bessie. But this wise dog, sensing how outrageous was the weather with whistling winds piling the stinging snow in unmanageable drifts, rashly made a dash for safety. Wise and foolish Bessie—wise in knowing better than to face the terrible storm, but foolish in attempting to evade her persistent master, rushed through the kitchen, the dining room, and into the living room where she crawled under the davenport to hide. With his scarf flying, his unbuttoned overshoes flapping, red of face, and grumbling uncouth words under his breath, that most persevering of hunters followed. Bessie was not about to yield. Getting down on his hands and knees, Uncle Leonard, now shouting in sheer frustration, finally managed to get a grip on the poor dog's collar. He jerked her out of her place of concealment by brute force. Carrying her in one arm and pummeling her with his free hand, he went into the kitchen where he freed the shivering hound after he had opened the outside door. Groveling in a corner on the rear porch, knowledgeable Bessie still refused to venture out into the storm. By this time every occupant of the house had become Uncle Leonard's laughing audience with each and everyone making pertinent suggestions. With a final, "Oh, to hell with it," the durable sportsman returned with the rest of us to the warmth of the kitchen. Poor Bessie has now gone to her just reward in that great dog kennel up in the sky, but I for one shall never forget her. Neither will I forget her flashing white teeth under a curled and snarling lip; for good hunting dog she may have been, she also dearly loved to bite people, especially me.

Often when my notes are lying on my desk, Cecile will clandestinely glance through them and when I notice her, she will pick up a sheet and say, "You are NOT going to write about that!" And, believe me, there are a few rather earthy scenes perhaps better left untold.

Often in modesty I have concealed
Important facts that now should be revealed,
But helpless cries of anguish have appealed
For silence to keep my lips forever sealed.
Surely then I'll lose all power and wealth
Won't you take the power? I'll take the wealth!

Thus this quaint Sage comes to the end of another long and tiring day. Hoo boy, but it will seem good to sit down!

GEM

A DELIGHTFUL CEREMONY

Containing the scene of a delightful ceremony long since consigned to limbo. So thoroughly did this custom disappear that even its name is now practically unknown.

My dear ones,

It happened the first New Year's Eve, or possibly the second, of our occupancy of River Roost. On this particular festive evening a small group of relatives was watching the last few hours of that year slowly pass us by, sipping complacently on "tall, cold ones" as we did so. Manny and Lena, newly married, were with us. The night was cold and clear. Suddenly we were aroused by an unearthly clamor—a riotous clanging. The banging of pans and the clatter of cowbells, the shouts and the laughter confused and confounded us. However, the continuation of this raucous noise soon brought to us the realization that we were being subjected to a real old-fashioned charivari. (How do you like that spelling? Go ahead, look it up, see for yourself.) All of this was in honor of Manny, Cecile's only brother, and his new bride who had traveled from Illinois to spend the holidays with us.

Charivari is a word almost lost to our language, as

I was soon to learn. A dictionary is a very handy tool, but it is completely useless if you don't know how to spell the word which you are looking up. I didn't, nor did my regular dictionaries give me a hint, although I tried several variations. Finally going to my big two-volume job, which did offer: *chivaree* (no definition) corruption of *charivari*. So, I looked up that oddly spelled word and found: charivari– "origin obscure; a mock serenade or concert of discordant noises made with kettles, pans, horns, etc." "Discordant noises" was indeed what we were hearing so I knew that we were being 'chivareed,' all in honor of Manny and Lena. Like many other interesting customs descending to us from our pioneer ancestors, like barn raising, this one was slowly becoming obsolete, a victim of "Who has the time?"

So we opened the doors and welcomed the intruders to discover that they were headed by Uncle Ed and Aunt Eve accompanied by the balance of our local relatives. A charivari calls for the groom to either buy off his tormentors or to invite them in and play the part of an enthusiastic host. Since this was New Year's Eve and the first of a long line of parties that were to become a tradition, there was plenty of food and heady beverages so that all Manny had to do was to laughingly become the butt of the type of jokes that are a part of being a groom. While this was not the first, it was the last charivari that I had the joyful fun to be a part of.

So sayeth the Sage of an event that happened in the year of our Lord nineteen hundred and forty-nine, I think.

GEM

BIRDS IN THE WINTER

Wherein I return to give you a small glimpse of the birds that wintered at River Roost.

My dear ones,

One advantage of the virgin fluffy snow was the background it made for the wild birds which were constant visitors at our rude but popular feeding station. The snow provided a sharp contrast for the dark, rather drab bodies of the sparrows and the delicate blue of the agile, white-breasted nut hatch. This is the unusual bird who scampers down a tree, or in our case, a pole, head first. There is the pale orange breast and dark back of the tufted titmouse; there are gay salt and pepper downy woodpeckers with their wise looking red-flecked heads; the slate grey to almost blackish sheen of the juncos, as well as the brilliant crimson of the male cardinal and the dashing blue of the jays, a sassy and aggressive bird—a true thief. Sometimes we see the so-called red-bellied woodpecker whose belly is not red, but rather a pale and almost indiscernible pink; he also has a salt-and-pepper body with a slash of intense red running from his bill over his head, ending at the base of his neck. But of all these creatures the friendliest, the tamest of all, was the black-capped chickadee, who with a little coaxing would eat out of your hand.

In two pans on the clothesline poles we usually

placed large mesh-covered pieces of suet. The mesh was to prevent the thieving jays from flying away with most of the suet at one time. Into the poles we had driven four spikes on which we could push whole ears of corn. We would tramp out a place in the snow where we could throw assorted seeds for the ground feeders; more of this seed was also placed in the pans on top of the poles. It was amusing to watch the downy woodpecker crawl completely inside a beefbone, discarded by the dogs, where he would feast on the marrow.

The dogs would stand beneath the poles and longingly eye the suet just out of their reach. As the snows would continue to fall and the snow mounds would build up higher and higher under the poles, the hanging suet would come closer and closer to our waiting pups. If the winters were long and hard with enough snow, the dogs were usually successful eventually, but more often in their frustration they would simply chase the birds away and lick up the sunflower seeds. We must guard against that!

Chirp, chirp, cheep, cheep,
GEM

131

SKATING ON THE POND

Containing a view of how hard we work to play, or a fleeting view of winter.

My dear ones,

Our gravel pit was spring fed and as the gravel came out, the water flowed in, forming a considerable pond which froze in the winter . All of our friends and relatives would come with shovels and brooms to clear the snow from the ice, which was no little job considering the area to be cleared. If, after the first heavy freeze, the ice was kept clean, it was always smooth; but if it became covered with a blanket of snow which was allowed to remain for a few days, there would be just enough thawing under the snow to make the ice rough and covered with nasty bumps. You will readily perceive that it was work, and hard work, to have an ice pond fit for skating. Once the ice was cleaned, the games would begin. Watching from the picture window, it was great fun (and much warmer) to watch a stream of skaters "snap the whip." The last ones in the line would go flying off to land in a convenient snow drift, screaming with the sheer delight which young folks seem to find when in immediate, imminent, personal danger.

her newly pierced ears, defended my position by pointing out that Grandpa Bill would be more than happy to nurse the little fellow, having as you may recall, done so before. You may also recall the time when we were raising such a lamb in a huge cardboard box in the kitchen when the preacher came to call. As we attempted to entertain him in the living room talking of this and that, he suddenly said, "If I didn't know better, I would swear that I heard a lamb bleat." With our dignity completely swept away, we confessed that he was right and then showed him our charge. Dimly, perhaps you can hear Mother say, "This would, of all times, have to happen today!"

'Do ye ken what manner of a mon it be' who gathered all this questionable information and passed it on to you? 'Tis the Sage of River Roost, your own meek and charming, mild and erudite, gentle and modest,

and ever loving,
GEM

A SLOE GIN KIND OF PARTY

Relating a small portion of our lives where we are very honest and the proper word is used.

My dear ones,

Among many things which were disapproved of in our neighborhood were certain informal card playing parties, particularly if anything other than coffee was served. Hattie and Ed Lenart were good people, a kind and understanding couple. Hypocrites, they were not. A spade was always called a spade and even the minister was offered a drink if he made one of his infrequent calls at their house. Hattie and Ed had been excommunicated from the Reformed Church (kicked out, they called it) because Ed played his fiddle at barn dances.

All parties either begin or end in the kitchen, but the one we attended at the Lenarts' was spread all over the first floor of their farmhouse and extended into the basement (cellar was our word for it) where a bar of sorts was set up. This consisted mostly of a fifty gallon barrel of HARD cider complemented with sundry other alcoholic beverages. Harriet, Hattie's friend of many years, was enthusiastically endorsing her specialty, sloe gin. No fancy mixes for her; she drank this pink liquid straight. Satisfied with the clean sharp taste of Sloe Berries, she drank, not sipped, from a water glass.

"Watch it. That stuff will hit you," Harriet was warned. This, however, was only taken as an invitation to have another, which she did and did and did!

Hat, our thoughtful and attentive hostess, had gone upstairs to the kitchen to prepare a little lunch (cheeses, pickles, cold chicken, beef and pork, relishes, pie, cake and homemade breads). In the midst of these preparations she heard that frenetic shuffling of an inebriated person who doesn't think that anybody can recognize their condition, slowly coming up the basement stairs. Although it was very difficult to hear anything above the table thumping of euchre or the noisy bidding of pinochle, we still knew that Harriet was on her way to the kitchen. That last step was too much and she sprawled, her face as white as cold mutton, flat on the floor. Then she became sick. Hat, in a vain attempt to save her spotless floor, bodily dragged her guest into the adjacent bathroom and attempted to hold her head over the stool while she puked (that was Hattie's expression!). It was too much for that gem of hostesses. While Harriet was relieving her tortured stomach, Hat, still holding her guest, but no longer able to control her own nausea over this unpleasant business, was now puking down Harriet's back!

During the following month Harriet marvelled at her own dexterity at covering herself both front and rear. And then came the moment of truth.

"Why, Harriet, you didn't do that," Hat explained. "While you were puking in the can, it made me sick too and so I puked all over your back!"

Ref: Webster - *Puke, puking* (source unknown), vulgar, "to vomit."

Cecile has been wondering how I would handle this one. Let's just get a little fresh air!

Oh, such stories I tell,
GEM

STUTTERING ED

Relating a short biography of stuttering Ed and at the same time allowing you a hasty glimpse of Gus.

My dear ones,

"Get rid of the middleman! Hold the phone! The middleman gets all of the profit while the farmer starves." Thus did Ed Lenart vent his spleen against society by grouping all who seemed to promote difficulties, real or imaginary, for the common man. "Hold the phone" was his favorite and most easily enunciated expression. Lean, wiry and strong, Ed was a 139-pound, five foot, six-inch individual who said exactly what he thought should be said, come "Hades" or highwater," except that his conversation was never bound by such sissy words as "Hades!" He was more explicit. He was one of those rare persons who was a man apart and of parts: he stuttered. In the rush to properly express himself the words stuck, and in silent embarrassment you agonized with him through the long seconds it would take him to force his mouth to release a word, a sentence, a thought. Nevertheless, he was a thoughtful man. He was also a kind man, a good man, a strange man, different in all those peculiar and interest-

141

ing traits that made him so unforgettable. "Hold the phone! High, low Jack and the game-you're skunked!" That was the game, the ONLY game. The card game was over and Ed was the definite winner.

Ed was an extremely talented musician. While he could charm an audience on almost any instrument, he favored the guitar with which he accompanied himself while singing in a clear, strong voice of uncommon range. Strangely enough, he never stuttered while singing. His talent was always in demand at every square dance near and far. It was because of his easy acceptance of invitations to play at "these iniquitous affairs" that he was excommunicated by the straight-laced elders of the Dutch Reformed Church. It probably was because of this interdict that Ed, when meeting his former pastor, took enormous delight in instructing him in the benefits and enormous satisfaction in drinking beer and when the spirit prevailed, something stronger. It was his contention that the "Domini" was not above partaking of alcoholic beverages in secret. "Hold the phone" on that one!

Shortly after our entry into World War I, Ed was among the first soldiers to be bundled aboard a huge transport where he was to sleep on deck in his mismatched uniform while the ship was being conveyed to France.

Glamorous France! Ed was to see little glamour and little France. On his arrival he was packed into a "40 hommes or 8 chevou" box car and aimed at the front-line trenches. He was to live for weary days that dragged into months in a trench which was sandbagged at the top, with the bottom covered with a sticky, viscous mess of oozy mud which eventually came to be a part of his vermin-covered, dirty, perpetually cold body. Here he lived with tears, fears, prayers, and the hope that the constantly booming "Big Berthas" would not drop an exploding shell in his portion of the trench. Less than 100 yards away were the enemy trenches which shielded the "Boch"–the "Krauts." The area between was covered in an irregular manner with twisting strings of barbed wire and pitted with shell holes. "Over the top" was an order often given and often endured, an interlude between griping and smoking. Finally, when the dreary, bloody dream ended, he came home with his buddy Gus, a Polish American and a friend of many years; he came home in pride and joy to marry Hattie.

He bought a farm on the River Road which he started to work "the hard way" by plowing and cultivating with a team of horses, which he was soon to supplant with a tractor, but he never sold the horses. I suppose that they earned him an occasional dollar or two when he hitched them up to pull someone out of the mud which covered our terrible, ditchless road when we first moved into the neighborhood, but for the most part, the horses lived a life of indolent ease—just a chore for Gus to do. They were a symbol: they proved that he was a farmer, and he needed that symbol. After the Second World War to end all wars, the government began to put restrictions on what to grow and how much to grow, and farming ceased to be a way of life for the small operator. To supplement his meager earnings, Ed took a job in a foundry in Holland, some ten miles away.

The Lenarts owned two dogs. One was a black-and-white mongrel who barked at you when you drove into the yard. The other was a tiny, hairless, pop-eyed toy who would sit on Ed's lap, point his wee nose toward the ceiling and emit long, shrill noises, supposedly an accompaniment to Ed's singing, but sounding much more like a MAIDEN IN DISTRESS. (That wasn't supposed to be in caps, but I like the message it carries.) This mournful baying pup made Ed all the more popular and everyone thought that he had a "real smart dog."

Right after Ed's marriage, Gus, a short, squat man of Polish decent with a war-mutilated body, almost as badly mangled as the English he attempted to use, moved in with Ed. He was neither a hired man nor a boarder. He worked "cut by the day" and was in particular demand during the harvest season. This was also the time of the year that Ed needed him the most and this was the only time that a strained relationship ever appeared: Ed was working in the foundry and his own grain was ripe and Gus was "helping the neighbors." After the harvest, Gus was unusually busy. There was a great demand for firewood. Many of the farmers in our neighborhood still used wood for fuel for the kitchen range the year around, or at least in the early fall and spring. It was also needed for fireplaces. Gus "buzzed wood." On a trailer behind his decrepit car he had rigged up an ancient motor and a buzz saw. With these impliments he went from farm to farm to buzz a winter's supply of wood. This was a "mutual exchange of labor" proposition. "You help me get in my wood and I'll help you buzz." Gus ran the buzz saw for $1.50 an hour. He also received "coffee" in mid-morning, his lunch, and "coffee" in the afternoon. He never made much money at buzzing because his ancient equipment was constantly in need of either major or minor repairs, but he certainly enjoyed his work and his visits with the neighbors.

Hattie always attempted to keep something around for Gus to munch on. One day when she returned from shopping, she inquired whether or not Gus had had lunch. "Sure. I ate the corned beef hash that you had in the refrigerator." "Gus! You darn fool! That was canned dog food!"

Enough of this!
GEM

HATTIE AND ED

Relating how Hattie took advantage of Ed when he started to indulge too soon and alone.

My dear ones,

Our dear neighbors did tell us a good story the other day. Ed decided to celebrate secretly and in advance of a party that he and Hattie were planning to attend. He had procured a bottle of peppermint schnapps and began to take furtive sips. The better to do this he had hidden his bottle in the barn. Nipping on peppermint schnapps is difficult to conceal because its sticky aroma clings tenaciously to one's breath. Hattie, not one easily fooled anyway, soon discovered what was going on, and realizing that Ed could easily overdo his "occasional nips," she decided to do something about it. Shortly thereafter one of the neighbors dropped in as neighbors often do and Ed, the ever thoughtful host, invited Harold, the guest, to the barn on the excuse that he would like to show off his newborn calf. From its hiding place he withdrew the bottle of schnapps and invited Harold to have a drink. "Gosh, Ed, this tastes just like water.." "Well, it's not water; that's real schnapps. Have some more. Take all you want." "It still tastes like water," Harold insisted. "Let me have that bottle," stuttered Ed. He tilted the bottle and spat out a mouthful on the barn floor and rushed for the house calling for Hat. He found her in the kitchen doubled up with laughter. It took Ed a little while, after Hattie explained that she kept adding flavored water to his schnapps, to see the humor of the situation, but it finally dawned upon him and he began to smile. Then the real schnapps was brought out and Harold and Ed had their nip after all.

Your River Roost Sage,
GEM

down into the attic and into the bathroom and into the bedrooms.

Our yard now began to look like an auction sale. It seemed like hundreds of people (probably not half that many) had followed the fire trucks as people have always followed fire trucks, and thronged into our yard where, with the help of the neighbors as well as total strangers, we were carrying outside in an aimless, disorganized fashion, pieces of furniture and clothing. One of the first pieces to be carried out was, of course, the stuffed bear cub—that, it seemed must be saved before all else! Everything was deposited in a helter-skelter manner all over the yard. Everywhere was chaos and confusion. Through this shambles I floated futilely from one object to another while my stunned mind kept insisting that what was happening just couldn't be happening to us. It was all so unreal. This was something that could only happen to someone else—never to us. Then it was all over! The calm that now descended on River Roost was as enervating as that of our first knowledge of this catastrophe. The fire department had left and our solicitous friends soon followed. We slowly awakened from this foreboding dream and surveyed the wreckage which was still permeated with the stink of wet smoke, an aroma that was to last years.

Somehow the ceiling didn't want to stop leaking. Leaking? A steady stream of water cascaded down from the beam closest to the fireplace and filled tub after tub with dirty, smoke-stained water. Then it dawned on us that the bathroom lead pipes had melted from the terrific heat. We remedied this wet situation by hunting out and shutting off the upstairs water supply from a basement valve, but the living room remained a dirty jumble of wet litter. The carpet was a complete ruin and the wallpaper, beams, and woodwork were water and smoke stained. We hung blankets over the arch to close off the living room from the rest of the house.

The top floor was an absolute mess. Everything in the boys' and the girls' rooms was water soaked, stained and smelled to high heaven of smoke. Our bedroom was in a worse, if that's possible, condition. We set up a temporary bed in the basement for Ted and Terry (Terry now came to visit) and the slats of their bed were constantly falling out and spilling two groaning boys out onto the cold, hard basement floor where they called to us to come and rescue them. Somehow we slowly began to organize our lives around the necessity of reconstruction and making some semblance of living a normal, but for the present, a rather dismal life. We made many arrangements to repair the tremendous damage. A brighter side of life began to emerge: we had Thanksgiving over an open fireplace, open to the great outdoors, and we had hot dogs for Christmas that year.

Most of the severe damage had been confined to the northeastern part of the house, where a huge gaping hole in the roof opened upon all of the bathroom, and a large part of the girls' room where the east wall had completely collapsed. The outside wall of the bathroom was open to the cold breezes of a great Michigan winter and the floor of this valuable room where I had been sitting on that fateful morning was nonexistent, just a big charred hole staring into the living room. The fire had apparently started from wayward sparks from the fireplace which had over time ignited the rafters in the attic.

The morning after the fire consisted of several hours of woebegone, nervous waiting, but the early afternoon brought those good fairies of the worried and the harried, the insurance adjusters There were two earnest - faced men who, after introductions, tramped through the house, and while emitting a few "Ohs" here and "Ahs" there, they displayed an unusual lack of interest in the damage. Their inspection trip ended with this surprising and certainly unexpected statement, "We have done a lot of checking on you people and you seem to be quite honest. Why don't you go ahead and fix everything up as good as it was before the fire. Keep a good record of the expenditure and we'll pay all the bills." WOW! The feeling of relief that settled on two McNitts was like coming out of an anesthetic and realizing that you are going to live after all. There were, of course, a few qualifications, but only a few. Our living room carpet, as an example, was ruined and had to be replaced, but we had to allow for the years of wear it had already had against the life expectancy of a new carpet, a very fair arrangement. The next day, the contractor and his crew moved in. Reconstruction started. Every move that we made, it seemed, disclosed something new to be repaired, reclaimed, or scrubbed. Smoke had seeped through the rafters to every part of the house. Even the dishes in the pantry on the extreme southwest part of the house were soot covered. Every piece of clothing and bedding had to be laundered or dry cleaned, and a year later many of them still smelled of smoke! The insurance company agreed to pay the going labor rate if we wanted to do the decorating ourselves, and we did. Cecile bent over backwards to be fair, charging only $1.50 an hour for her services, a small enough fee, but she gloried in her wallpapering ability, and she was good. All damaged parts and pieces had to come out or down before the new could replace them. We started in a mess and we were still in a mess three months later, but we were making some headway.

With all the hurly-burly and anxiety of the first day of the fire, we forgot to notify Chum in college at Michigan Tech up in Houghton. He had to learn about the fire from one of his friends who wrote to him all about the affair. Long were we condemned for this, and rightly so.

The rest of the world didn't stop moving on our account, but it kept right on sailing around and around and the people who inhabited it were busy with their own affairs. One of these people was Nadine, nephew Merlin's dear wife, who at that time was "infanticipating" for what would become Stevie. Cecile had previously planned a stork shower for her, and now Aunt Ruth offered to have the party, but Cecile felt that everyone would want to see the ruins anyway and so her plans went forward. The party was held with blankets closing off the living room and it spoke much for Cecile's genius that nothing seemed to faze her. She could entertain regardless of the circumstances which might from time to time confront her.

Seven and one half tons of a special hard sandstone

157

went into the new fireplace, which was the biggest single repair job, completely new from the ground up. The sandstone was used because we couldn't find a mason competent to work with field stone, and the mason that we ended up with was a "doozy." He always wore a stocking cap inside out and he was always late, but he was an excellent craftsman.

We had a Christmas tree given to us that year but somehow it never got put up. There just didn't seem to be a suitable place for it, and Myrna Lee still bemoans and belabors that fact. I doubt if we will ever be forgiven. Christmas Day, our twenty-fifth anniversary day as well, was spent in papering the living room where this provident husband presented his paperhanging spouse twenty-five beautiful yellow rose buds to commemorate the occasion. They held a place of honor, a flash of gold on a corner of the grand piano, overlooking the mess.

Three months and seventy-five hundred dollars later, we began to clean up after the last of the carpenters, and the furniture and the people began to fall into their rightful places.

We finally had our home back again. Amen!

GEM

What will I do when all of this is done
And there are no more honors to be won?
Meekly bow my head and ask your pardon
For trying with my comments you to con?
Through all your deals you thought that you
were cute.
Why yes, I'll take your note, but what's to boot?
(May your Sage suggest that one phrase will distinguish
all of these verses: Keep your heart right and be not
greedy!)

The Mc Nitt Family By The Fireplace

AN ANSERINE LESSON

This saga, important in the history of River Roost, tells how some large birds, whose necks were shorter than their bulky bodies, came strutting into our lives and affection in order to show that their name, which is sometimes used to describe a "silly person," should not be so used.

My dear ones,

It was, I think, during the second summer of our life on the farm that several families (trios) came into our lives and securely captured our hearts. They came by way of Aunt Eve and Uncle Ott and were our introduction to that bewitching, often humorous, and always interesting business of raising geese. A nearby poultry man, hearing about our entrance into this field, prevailed upon us to accept a "bargain" of forty young geese, slightly less than two years old, which, added to the other more mature birds gave us an excellent start toward fame and fortune.

I was attempting, one day the following spring, to put a window in the second floor of our barn. To do this, I bored a hole in the siding of the barn and continued with the help of various tools to enlarge this opening. I was hammering, sawing, and making, in my fumbling, amateurish way, an infernal racket. Perhaps twenty feet below me, one of our geese had yielded to her natural instincts and was "setting" on a clutch of twelve eggs. The noise which I was making apparently bothered her, for from time to time, she would emerge from her nest and peer up at me in disgust. I little considered the importance of her job, engrossed as I was in mine, and so I continued to saw and hammer in my futile ignorance of the trade of carpentry. Her patience finally exhausted, Madam Goose stalked out of the old vinegar barrel which lay a third buried in the moist earth and partially filled with straw, to give a loud and urgent squawk exactly as any other embarrassed or infuriated female might. It seemed that hardly a minute had elapsed when, his tranquil swim on the river interrupted, a huge and vociferous gander, half flying, half running, joined her. He listened a moment to her complaint, and then, raising and cocking his eyes at me, he shrieked out a most severe warning. Madam Goose went back to her nest in the barrel, ruffling her feathers to cover her clutch of eggs. She left the matter of her safety in the capable wings of her husband, who paraded back and forth in front of the barrel muttering and grumbling.

Early each spring we would set traps to protect our poultry from the ever-increasing depredations of the clever and hungry raccoons whose educated little fingers could open any ordinary latch or catch. Our trapping produced unexpected, unusual, and unnecessary results. The first day, we caught our spindly legged heifer, who ruined the trap. The next day, aroused by a dreadful shrieking, I rushed out to discover that our largest gander had become caught in our coon trap. At this time, we had by purchase, but mostly by natural increase, accumulated a flock of over two hundred geese. With the exception of this greedy gander whose inquisitiveness was to get him into trouble, the entire flock had grazed their way down to the river where they now could be heard splashing and gossiping while they enjoyed their swim. A Toulouse gander is a very large bird with the strength in his tremendous wings sufficient to most easily break an arm or a leg of a mere human. This huge gander with an instinctively superior knowledge was very docile while I sprang the trap to release him. I picked him up in my arms and carried him back to the goose yard where he properly belonged and where I carefully set him down. He hobbled painfully about for a few seconds, looked at me as though asking my permission and then he emitted a long, penetrating call. From the river, a quarter of a mile away, he was promptly answered. Within minutes our entire goose population had joined

162

him; some flying, some running, all talking. In a large circle, they surrounded him while he explained, with an occasional glance in my direction as though asking for verification for his story, his agonizing experience. This was only one of many fascinating examples which not only prove the intelligence of geese, but also proves conclusively that they have the ability to talk, or at least to carry on a conversation.

Geese are, even as you and I, great gossips and scandalmongers. If unmolested, geese will mate for life and remain faithful, one to the other, usually forming a trio: a gander and two geese. There are no secrets within a flock of these interesting birds. When a gander mates with one of his wives, the entire flock will surround them, and

Scandalmongers

in their high-pitched, almost shrieking voices, they will tell all the world about such scandalous proceedings, scandalous only to humans—normal and natural to all "more intelligent" beings.

Unless excited or frightened, the domestic goose, unlike his wild relatives, prefers to walk rather than to fly. While he is quite capable of flying, and does so on occasion, his well-fed body is much too large for him to take comfort or delight in that exercise. Because of this preference for walking, geese can be herded like cattle and driven from place to place and, also like cattle, when given good pasture they will graze contentedly with little else necessary in the form of food to sustain them. In addition to regularly seeded pasture, they love the tender new shoots of crab and quack grass as well as all ordinary weeds. For this reason they have been used very successfully in weeding strawberry patches, marching up and down the rows with their heads bobbing and their bills pecking at each new weed or grass shoot. While they have no appetite for the tough leaves of the strawberry plant, they do love the juicy berries; consequently, it is not wise to leave a goose in the patch when the berries start to form, and most certainly not when they ripen! Furthermore, this works only when the strawberries are separated from the rest of the garden, because these intelligent creatures are also extremely fond of other garden goodies: lettuce, young corn!

Even with the almost constant use the legs are the weakest part of a goose's body and are easily broken. The enormous strength of his wings, however, can be a terrible weapon when angered. A wise person will think twice before bothering a gander or his mate at nesting time, for they will surely fly at you with their wings flailing in order to protect their family or their family-to-be. If, however, one grabs a goose by her wings at that point which is the closest to its body, the poor bird is then completely incapacitated and readily surrenders. How do you get that close to those flailing powerhouses? Well, you come in sideways, pray, and grab real fast!

It is a fine spectacle to watch a flock of geese coming up from the river, marching in a precise military manner that took no drilling to perfect. In a yard especially set aside for them, twice daily, morning and night, we slowly poured on the ground in a long semicircle, pails of corn, to which, with much squabbling and yammering, the geese abandoned themselves, a sight which never failed to entertain us.

By the use of considerable dexterity, proper balance,

and another prayer, we finally learned how to pluck the soft feathers and down from live geese. What fun!

Since it is almost impossible to tell the sex of a goose (the depth of the shade of orange on their bill!), we, of necessity, had to learn how to accomplish this unusual act. Rather, I should say, Cecile, with instruction given by a very dear friend, an "Old Country" Polish lady, a true daughter of the soil, who, we discovered, was a veritable fount of unusual and mysterious knowledge. It was long after, and with considerable reluctance, that Cecile was persuaded to allow me to become initiated into this select company of GOOSE SEXERS! It was necessary to learn this peculiar art because our new goslings were divided almost equally as to their sex and we had no need for the extra ganders, you see. Associating with geese grows in indefinable pleasure as time elapses.

One wise old goose hid her nest, and so, one day she took us completely by surprise by proudly walking into the goose yard followed by fourteen downy, yellow goslings. Naturally, the entire flock had to circle around the new-comers for a thorough inspection before noisily voting to accept the little fellows, but mother goose was very firm about the matter and so they became an integral part of our ever-growing flock. They had no problems until they grew older and had to compete for their share of corn which then made it necessary for them to move just a little bit faster than their elders.

Most of our goose eggs were gathered daily, dated with a marking pencil, and stored for four or five days while we decided on a mother for them: a broody goose, a broody rock hen, or the incubator, all having some good features. By our picking up the eggs daily, a goose will continue to lay much longer than she normally would if she were allowed to accumulate a "clutch" of eggs, which would usually total twelve to fourteen eggs, all that she could cover comfortably. When the eggs are picked up regularly, the poor goose is teased into laying an additional clutch. Would this be cheating? The difference between a broody goose and a broody hen is, of course, largely, the number of eggs which each bird can cover. They also talk differently (a goose has a larger vocabulary!) Oh, there is one other very important difference. If a goose has made her nest near water, she can then handle her 'setting' problem without any other help, excepting, perhaps, the guard duty which she often calls upon her husband to perform. She will carefully turn her eggs several times a day and by frequent swims, she will transfer the dampness of her feathers to her eggs—a necessity for a good hatch. A broody hen, even a large one, can handle only four or possibly five eggs at a time, but three is better. (I went down hill on that one, didn't I?) A broody hen, however, needs help. Because of the size of a goose egg–they weigh from six to eight ounces (an eight-ounce egg, coming from an older goose is by far the best,) the poor broody-hen cannot turn or dampen the eggs and consequently an artificial father like me, has to do the job for her. Never less than four, and usually six times a day, I would dampen (wet) my hand in warm water and reach under the uneasy and suspicious hen and thus supply the needed moisture and turn the eggs at the same time. Regardless of the method of incubation, all eggs need to be turned at regular intervals to prevent the embryo from sticking to the shell, and all eggs require moisture to prevent too fast evaporation of the eggs' contents. Goose eggs need more of this special attention. Incubation temperatures should never be allowed to go below 101 or over 103 degrees. Because of their weight, the goose eggs in our electric incubator had also to be turned by hand since the mechanical device would not do the job. It seemed to me, perhaps because of my small knowledge and experience, that we had to HELP an unusual number of goslings out of their shells at the end of the incubation period, which required from thirty to

168

thirty-two days before we became new parents. The feeling, when you first notice that a sharp beak has pecked a small opening in the protective shell and you realize that a new life, a new gosling, wants 'out,' is indescribable. Slowly, removing just a little bit of this tough shell at a time, we assisted into the world this new life. In contrast, because of her built-in ability and natural instincts, (she has supplied the proper conditions,) a goose needed no attention and was happier when left alone.

One time, after twenty-nine days of incubation, a flash electrical thunder storm hit our area, leaving us with one hundred, ready to be born dead baby goslings! Our kind Polish friend had warned us that such an event could very well happen, but we were much too sophisticated to believe in these 'Old Wives' Tales.' Now we are converted believers!

Those goslings which were hatched naturally by a mother goose were at once readily accepted by the flock of adult geese. Those which we hatched artificially in an incubator and hand fed for the first few days of life decided that we were the mother and the older geese snubbed them and chased them away. They shunted them aside with their long necks and yellow beaks, leaving us with several flocks to separately care for. In the late fall, with the approach of winter, the flocks united under a common front for protection against the time when the excess ganders were laboriously separated from the flock for the market. On one cold and unhappy morning, these intelligent birds decided that they had had quite enough of this nonsense, and under the generalship of an old and foxy gander they took to the air, flying to the river where much to our consternation, they were able to evade us until after New Year's Day, when these birds decided finally to forgive and forget. What a happy day it was when we saw that large flock, still wary, cautiously making their way through the snow toward the barn, pausing now and then to rest. We, for our part, lost no time in supplying them a double ration of corn, and from the depth of our hearts welcomed them home.

During the many years when we were raising geese we were fortunately free from predators, with the possible exception of the few eggs which were stolen by either the raccoons or skunks. We did, however have a fat, little black puppy which committed suicide when he was discovered grabbing our new goslings, shaking them thoroughly, and then dropping them to the ground, dead. When I saw what was happening, there was a flash of red flame through my brain and that little black puppy never knew what hit him!

Geese reach their best productive years after they are five years old, and they live for thirty-five or more years with a constant increase of knowledge. We built our flock of birds up to where they numbered over 325 geese when my illness and consequent need for money made it necessary to part with them. I have constantly regretted their absence ever since that time!

All this has come to you from that second-in-command, a goose sexer, at River Roost.

GEM

SKIPPY, THE PUP

Containing a short biography of but one in a long series of many of "man's best friends," about whom there have been issued a multitude of false statements, that it behooves me, in a small way to come to his defense.

My dear ones,

Skippy never, under any circumstance, allows Taffy to get more than a few feet away from him and when she, that is Taffy, is "that way," he crowds even closer to her, as if it were possible to do so. Every time that "this time" comes, Cecile, of course, insists that Taffy is going to have puppies, an event that has never happened, and in all probability never will happen because of the vast difference in the size of these two animals: a fact of life which deflates Skippy's ego. This at least accounts for their very close relationship.

They daily create a major disturbance among our wild bird friends. Taffy, as is the case with most females, rules the roost with a most autocratic paw. She takes over the dog house where she carefully hides and protects her many bones so that Skippy, trying always to be near her, must, of necessity, sit right smack on the spot where, in the winter, we always throw the bird seed, in order that all the feathered folk, the ground feeders as well as others, might have an equal opportunity to enjoy our hospitality. He not only sits there, but he also eats the sunflower seeds, scraping them up with his paw while he looks longingly up at the suet in a pan high on a pole above him. It matters not how rough and tough the weather may be, Skippy remains glued to that spot, creating no little unrest among our feathered friends, while the jays, in particular, use some rather ribald language, and from other shrill sounds, I also suspect, that this same angry profanity is coming from all the birds. This unhappy condition exists until Taffy emerges from the dog house to lead Skippy off on a hunting expedition which, more often than not, is down in the river bottoms where high water has landlocked some carp. When finally the dogs return, they are covered with river mud as black as sin and they also "smell to high heaven."

Contrary to certain common and malicious rumors, Skippy is not "dumb." The fact that he stands on his hind legs, jumping up on people, both large and small, is only indicative of his desire to emulate the human species. He just craves affection. Skippy's name, of course, derives from a lustful father who spent only part of one day on the farm, and then skipped out, as men often do!

It is true, he sometimes chases cars, but only to protect the farm and family from an invasion by those rattling, banging, and fume-spewing mechanical monstrosities which sometimes come down the forest's narrow gravel road.

We have discovered that by keeping just one of the dogs chained (we use a long chain) at all times, they both remain at home instead of going roaming, we know not where. They are changed daily at feeding time so no hardship is imposed on them and they are now so well trained that, on call, they come and lie down, the easier to effect the "changing of the guards." Skippy is first in the affections of Cecile, and well he knows this, so whenever he sees that kind lady, he promptly starts to whine, and then Cecile "let's him off the hook."

"He begged so hard," she says. Winning this easy victory, off they go at once to the river bottoms again! While awaiting their smelly return, I remain your affectionate Sage of the Roost,

GEM

POACHERS!

An exposure of a baneful practice, practiced by some men who had scant regard for the law.

My dear ones,

When I answered the door on a cold, cloudy afternoon in early December, I was confronted by a total, but agreeable appearing stranger. Since nearly everyone was a stranger during our first few months at River Roost, this was not surprising. A friendly smile and the offer of a handshake came with: "I am Mr. S__ from Saugatuck. Would you mind if I went hunting? My answer was as easy and gentle as the stranger's smile, for I wanted to be friendly. "Not at all. Help yourself." With my answer, Mr. S__ started to move away in the direction of the river and had perhaps gone fifty feet when he turned and called,

"Do you like goose?" and before I could answer, he added, "Good. I'll see you in a little while." and he walked away in his hip boots as soft, slowly falling snow assisted the fast approaching darkness in obscuring him. In somewhat less than an hour, as I was gazing out of our picture window, he reappeared out of the early dusk and tapped on the door. "Here you are," he announced as I opened the door. He handed me a still warm Canada goose. "But, I don't want to take your game," was my mildly resisting reply. "Oh, that's all right. I have six more! Whenever you come over to Saugatuck, stop in and I'll give you some fish."

This was my first introduction to the game outlaws of Allegan County. I was to find out there were many and they were as varied as the game which they poached, the most important of which was the white-tailed deer and the Canada goose, both of which seemed to offer a tremendous challenge to the unlawful instincts of poachers.

In the cold sharp nights of winter we were often awakened by gunshots reverberating through the frosty air. Our back roads abounded with traffic. Slowly driven cars with their spotlights waving from one side of the trail to the other, searching for that telltale flash of reflection coming when the light would shine into the eyes of a helpless deer, kept roaming throughout the woods until the small hours of morning. The crashing boom of a high-powered rifle would tell us that some luckless doe had fallen, a victim to greed.

Although the game authorities were quite aware of the conditions which prevailed in the Allegan State Forest, they seemed unable to cope with the insatiable meat-hungering hunter. The unlawful hunt for wild geese had taken on the quality of a game between the wardens and the poachers. A boatload of outlaws would go up the river to make their kill and then, before returning, one or two of the party would leave the boat, walking through the dense brush in the bottom land until they reached one of the sandy back roads where they would be picked up by a waiting car and safely stow their illicit gain out of sight. Meanwhile the rest of the party would float "innocently" down the river to a point (Raleigh's shack) where they would be intercepted by disconsolate, disgusted, and frustrated game wardens.

Enough of the bad guys!
GEM

OUTLAWS

A few more words about outlaws...

My dear ones,

There was a group of men who often came hunting in our area who, while not really full-fledged outlaws, were borderline, or occasional outlaws, not yet having crossed the line on a permanent basis. They always purchased their licenses and tried all legal methods to fill them, but when they had exhausted these procedures and had bagged no game, it took very little persuasion for them to try something just a little "extra" legal.

One of these men, a good friend of both the outlaws and the near-outlaws, was wealthy L__, who devoted his life to the hunt whether it was in Michigan, Wyoming, or wherever big game was available. Each year, usually about deer season, L__ came calling, bearing a gift of a fifth of excellent Scotch in appreciation for his hunting privileges. L__ would present me with the bottle, and naturally I would offer him a drink which he just as naturally accepted and he then remained, sitting comfortably at our kitchen table, until the bottle was down to the last two inches before finally departing. The look in my dear

Cecile's eye said it all, "What kind of a gift was that?"

More often than not, when L__ called, several of the executives (near-outlaws) of a now defunct company in Holland, would also drop in with their bottles, accompanied by their friends and then wild hunting stories poured out quite as fast as the booze was poured!

And you wondered how I knew so much about all this outlawing, didn't you?

I remain your honorable

GEM

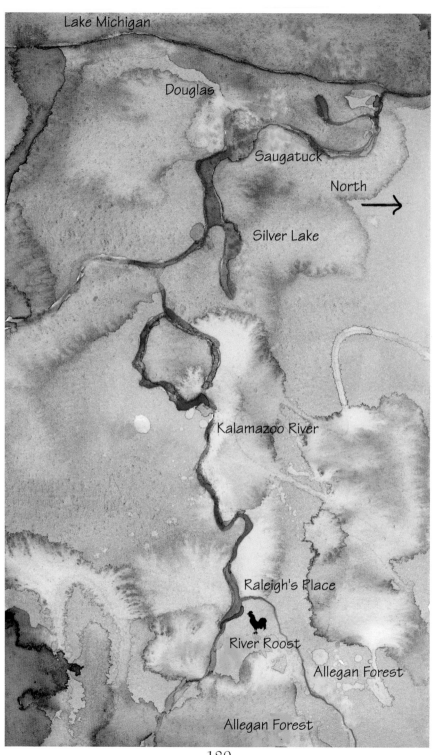

Lake Michigan

Douglas

Saugatuck

North →

Silver Lake

Kalamazoo River

Raleigh's Place

River Roost

Allegan Forest

Allegan Forest

180

JERRY, THE STEER

An apology for our embarrassment because we allowed ourselves to be outwitted by a dim-wit!

My dear ones,

From the first day that Jerry, a four-hundred pound steer (a bull that has lost his manhood before he ever knew that he had any) came to graze and grow fat (we hoped) at River Roost, he seemed to exude a certain sly, wild, unsocial behavior. There was a shifty, glassy look in his eyes and a wary manner in his actions that presaged broken fences and other unseen, unhappy events to come. Any thoughts that we may have had in regard to this animal were all bad. He soon proved to be mean, stubborn and quite unappreciative of any offer of kindness. He performed every vile trick that any animal could possibly conceive or invent on the spur of the moment. He was vicious, unbalanced and suffering from many irrational animal delusions—in short, he was a schizophrenic. Now, maybe the word *schizophrenic* is reserved only for humans: if so, let's call him crazy, for if any animal ever was crazy, Jerry most certainly was. Perhaps, because our IQ was slightly higher, we managed to out-wit him, or we thought that we did, more

181

than he out-witted us. With this small advantage in our favor, never relaxing our vigilance, he grew in bodily size, but his mean, crafty, demented brain, if it grew at all, grew only in the variety of intellectual quirks which his schizophrenic brain could foist upon us. In all of our experiences at River Roost we had never owned an animal which caused us so much additional and unnecessary work as did this mentally and physically emasculated animal; and when, after a heavy graining and fattening period in the fall it came time for slaughtering, we were far from unhappy.

Of course, we had trouble driving him in from the pasture and into a stanchion for this heavy feeding period. And, of course, he wrecked the stanchion after we had tricked him into its confinement. But obstacles to overcome and problems to solve were a part of our daily life, and finally Jerry settled down to clean up his ever-increasing quantity of grain. Then came THE DAY!

We were unable that winter to do our own butchering and so we had decided to have him trucked to a local slaughterhouse. The trucker arrived with his able assistant. Before releasing Jerry from his stanchion these two strong men double roped him around his head and with a man holding a rope on each side, they led him out of the barn toward the truck; but Jerry, his wild eyes flashing, never even came close to the truck. At the very moment that he stepped out of the barn, he gave a tremendous bellow, and shaking his head belligerently he started to move, jerking forcibly from one side to the other. It was impossible to hold this animal who now weighed over a thousand pounds. With an enormous bound, he cleared our five-foot barnyard fence, and trailing his ropes behind him, he was off through the heavy snow and into the dense, dark woods.

I have often had the privilege of watching a deer gracefully jump over a high fence, but the sight of a thousand-pound steer whose feet were unusually clumsy, clear a five-foot fence without touching it was a sight to behold, albeit an unhappy one.

All day, through the snow and cold, we tracked our recalcitrant Jerry, catching an occasional glimpse of him; but he was too wary, too wild, and too crazy to permit us to close in on him. With visions of poor Jerry slowly starving to death in the cold and heavy snow of an unusually hard winter, we thought that he was gone for good!

A few days previous to this debacle a very unfortunate and sad incident had occurred. The child of one of our close friends had lost her life in an automobile accident and we felt that it was imperative to attend her funeral, which was to take place the following day. That evening, tired and discouraged from our fruitless effort to find the escaped Jerry, we called on a few of our neighbors whose farms were in the vicinity of the woodland where our steer had taken refuge, asking each one to advise us if they should by chance spot him. Hearing that we had intended butchering this (I'm still convinced that he was crazy) animal, they became more than normally interested. Since they all enjoyed hunting, they inquired if we cared if they shot him. This was more than acceptable to us, anything to salvage what we could from the mess in which we now found ourselves. Thus it was, while we attended a funeral, that the Great Steer Hunt was organized.

Unless one has lived in a farm community, it is hard to understand the kindness and thoughtfulness that motivates the movements of one's neighbors. The Great Steer Hunt, we were to discover, had become a community project. Jerry had been hunted down, shot, dressed out after he had been dragged out of the woods, and hung up in our barn. When we returned that evening, there he hung, all dressed in a professional manner, ready to be cut up into roasts and steaks! This was one more of the many examples of graciousness exhibited by the wonderful people we were happy to call neighbors and friends.

Later, of course, we entertained these good people at a huge steak dinner, feasting on that CRAZY Jerry!

Wishing you were there,
GEM

Jerry's Trail

PICKLES

Shows how desperate desires for new luxuries accompanied by the importunities of your offspring can trap one into unyielding drudgery.

My dear ones,

Hoo boy, my aching back! (You can say that again!) OK – Hoo boy, my aching back! In our incessant search for additional funds we finally lit upon a project, which we simply called "Pickles." Astonishingly enough, we found this enterprise profitable, and it needed to be to offset the extremely backbreaking, arduous work. We were warned, but heeded not that warning. The contracting processor furnished the seed and promised to take the entire crop, on a graded basis, of course. They kept their agreement and they were most fair in their grading, with the highest price being paid for the tiny gerkins. The price continued downward as the size of the pickle increased until they reached the dill size, which paid the least amount of the hard coin of the realm. While our planting was less than an acre it was actually a large area to work for our small and occasionally uncooperative group.

After the soil was properly prepared, we planted the seed and then discovered that the weeds grow as fast as and often times faster than the pickles. Nevertheless, we watched with great enthusiasm for the new plants to make their appearance. We relentlessly cultivated, and we hand-weeded around the young plants as we thinned them, working with them daily as they grew and expanded, running here and there until they finally broke into blossom. It seemed that hardly any time passed from the appearance of a little yellow bloom until the first tiny gerkin told us that the plants were in production. Once started, the pickles grew so rapidly that we were in a constantly hunched position in order to keep abreast of the harvest. Daily we searched the vines, our hands becoming raw and stained from the sharp barbs on the pickles, and our backs shrieked in agony from the constant bending position necessitated by this incessant picking. When the pickles arrived at the processors they were placed in a brine bath until, at some future date, they would be manufactured into any of dozens of different styles. All things, both good and bad must eventually come to an end. Our pickle crop did—and so did we. Thankful to again walk upright, we took our accumulated checks and purchased our first television! [We all sat down, munching popcorn balls, to watch our first episode of *The Lone Ranger*.]—ed.

Thanks for aching with us!

GEM

Our First Television

A LESSON WELL LEARNED!

Wherein we learn the dire results of playing with
matches and resolve to profit therefrom.

My dear ones,

On a balmy, spring-scented Saturday in one of our
first years at River Roost, we had carefully raked all the
leaves in our yard, carrying the smaller piles to a larger one
where we carefully burned them. Previously, and fortunately, we had secured a permit to burn from the fire warden who was usually found perched high in his tower overlooking the Allegan State Forest. The warm earth yielded
up pleasant odors full of a promised greenery. Relieved of
its winter accumulation of trash, we thought that the daf-
fodil-bordered yard looked very fine. Living as we did, surrounded mostly by venerable oak trees which were still
shedding their leaves when spring came, we were always
faced with a monumental task of disposing of an accumulation of broken branches and leaves. It was late afternoon
when we finished with this troublesome job and congratu-
lated ourselves on its completion. Then, with what we
thought was a flash of genius, we decided to make the yard
more attractive still by burning the dry grass in front of
our picture window. A very gentle breeze was blowing from
the east and so we started small grass fires from that direction. This breeze, however, suddenly became a wind and

A Forest Fire

190

our tiny grass fires became a holocaust which swept across our yard faster than Man of War could run. It rushed into our meadow of perhaps thirty acres, which was surrounded on the far western end by dense woods, on the south by the river, and on the north by the county road bordered by twenty or thirty feet of dense brush and trees. Across the road, also to the north, was more of the wild woodland for which Allegan County was famous. Like an avalanche, the fire cascaded into our fields, and before heading southwesterly, it rushed north to ignite the brush along the road. One spark across that narrow thirty foot road and all of Allegan County would be ablaze!

We fought with every meager resource available. Our pitiful garden hose was useless. We used wet sacks and we shoveled sand. We carried water. When we were fortunate enough to stem the fire at one point, it broke out anew farther away at some unguarded point. We shouted to one another in a vain attempt to organize our efforts. We cried real tears which mingled with our sweat to streak our soot-covered anxious faces. Out of the depths of desperation, Cecile took our car and drove madly away to our neighbors for much-needed help and also to call the fire warden. He had already seen our plight from atop his tower. Cecile returned with our faithful neighbors carrying more shovels and wet bags, and our frantic work continued. Carrying more water, we futiley and blindly fought this crazy blaze which roared relentlessly on. We gagged.

191

We burned ourselves and we cried some more!

We were at the westem edge of our meadow, perhaps one hundred feet from our woods and real danger, when we heard the siren. Gasping huge sighs of relief we watched that monster truck come crashing through our fence, knocking down small trees and brush which would have stopped a smaller piece of machinery. Using modern fine-spray nozzles, water was thrown under tremendous pressure over that long line of fire which had so terrified us. Within only fifteen minutes the ugly blaze was extinguished and the Allegan Forest was saved!

In the many eventful years since then, we never again burned leaves or grass. We learned instead to build compost piles which proved of great value to our rich but light soil.

While this "office work" is very hard, there nevertheless will be MORE! Just you wait! Don't go away!

More from River Roost,
GEM

A LITTLE QUESTION

Wherein we study a bit of history in order to prove that there is nothing new under the sun. Here also, Kay, in learning about the facts of life, astounds and confounds her father with her depth of perception.

My dear ones,

I have recently been doing a bit of research (a much more intriguing word than reading) on the history of ancient Greece, which, beginning in Crete, reveals some very amazing and interesting parallels. Throughout its origin, growth, maturity and decline, their civilization, which had its beginning over 3,000 years before the birth of Christ, often exceeded our own culture and presented the same problems which disturb us today. Thus, I am forced to wonder if the 'Dads' of this opulent society did not also have the same sometimes embarrassing difficulty when they explained to their children the "whys and the wherefores."

When confronted with the necessity of explaining sex to my children, I have always tried, as the BOOKS so instructed, to give honest and direct, but not necessarily elaborate answers to the questions which they tossed to me.

193

One day as I was performing that one farm chore which can never be delayed or postponed, milking, Kay raised her first question on this vital subject. "Where do calves come from?" I was asked. "From the mother cow's belly," was my quick and "rather proud of myself answer." "Yes, I know that, Dad, but how do they get inside there?"

It was very cold that day, and the question froze and is still hanging in the frosty air.

This bit of edification comes to you direct from that mystified monarch of River Roost.

GEM

TEDDY AND HIS CHORES

A short article worthy of serious perusal, for in it is explained the necessity of constant study in order to keep informed on our rapidly changing world. It also shows the application of physical agility while applying mental concentration.

My dear ones,

Teddy accepted the chore of milking Daisy, our patient, brown-eyed Jersey, every morning and every evening after school without the slightest evidence of disapproval, and we wondered why. To get up sufficiently early to amble aimlessly and slowly out to the barn to attend to this bovine pet of ours and still arrive, fresh-washed and combed, at school on time, was no mean feat. We also wondered why it should take him such an extremely long time to accomplish an act which should have been completed in just a few minutes.

After calling repeatedly to him one morning at the top of my voice, to tell him that he would be late for school if he didn't hurry, and receiving no answer, I set angrily out for the barn, the better to put a fatherly prod to my second son. Teddy was milking. Seated comfortably on a milk stool with a book propped against Daisy's expansive stomach, with a cat on his left knee and with the milk pail between both knees, Teddy was accomplishing the unheard-of feat of reading, milking, and feeding the cat at the same time! With one hand it was alternately "zoom" to the milk pail and then "zoom" to the cat who awaited with an open mouth. The other hand was used to turn the pages of his book!

I dare say, there's a touch of Abe Lincoln in that boy.

GEM

UNCLE BUD AND A HAMMER

In which is offered the suggestion that the dubbing with a sword does not always create a true knight, nor does the gaining of a sheepskin necessarily make an electrical engineer and thus exposing that which has always been a most profound secret.

My dear ones,

One Sunday morning amidst the frantic rush to prepare for church, a problem arose. Sunday morning at River Roost is never a good morning for problems; for truly there goes on at that time a crazy, wild scramble. With every bathroom in use, breakfast to be prepared, chores to be done, tearful faces to be washed and unkempt hair to be combed, with "Sunday clothes" to be donned, we finally reach that stage of exhaustion where every nerve is completely raw, and I cannot help but wonder if God really approves of such actions. It was on one such wintry morning that I discovered that Daisy's automatic drinking cup had sprung a leak. Thus, of necessity, being excused from church attendance, I went to the barn equipped with the necessary plumbing tools to repair the damage. I had just completed this work when Chum came rushing to inform me that the motor on the furnace had apparently

197

gone bad and that the house was without heat. With one emergency job completed, I started another. By this time, Chum was also excused from church. So, with his assistance I disconnected the motor from the furnace in a wild, dreamy hope that in some miraculous way we might discover the trouble. Not only was the motor extremely hot, it appeared to be "up tight"and for some unnecessary, stubborn, balky reason it seemed to use its heated condition as an excuse for remaining idle. While I stood with my hands on my hips surveying this recalcitrant motor about which I knew less than nothing, my electrical engineer brother-in-law made his appearance. Cecile, before going on to church with the rest of the children, had called to inform Bud of our difficulties. He came well prepared with the proper tools and electric motors of various horsepower; in short, he had everything a good engineer might need. Bud took over.

"Well, now, let's see," he said. "First, we'll take off the pulley and examine the shaft and the bearings." However the pulley did not want to come off. It was stuck fast, frozen to the shaft. "Hmm--well now, that is odd," said the electrical wizard. Using a block of wood to protect the shaft, Bud took a hammer and began pounding in an attempt to release the pulley. No luck.. More pounding. More thoughtful "Hmms" and "Ahs." "Let's plug in the motor and see what will happen." When the connection was made, the motor ran perfectly. Apparently, when Bud pounded on the shaft, it was released. We replaced the motor on the furnace and it is still operating. All of this, of course, proves conclusively that one doesn't need a college degree to become an engineer. All one really needs is a hammer!

After the most profound meditation, I now offer as a valid premise the idea that in ANY type of engineering, a hammer is far more necessary than a degree. In final proof of which, I offer the following anecdote from which you will be able to draw the same conclusion.

For several years our constantly patient Sylvia, while driving a decrepit 1936 fenderless Chevrolet, always carried with her a hammer. When her car would stall, which it frequently did, she would jump out amid the honking of the exasperated drivers behind her who were thus delayed by her stalled car, and after giving three or four sharp blows on the carburetor with her educated hammer, she would nervously jump back into her car, step on the starter, and away she would go. You see, it took only a hammer to make her a successful automotive engineer!

Ergo, my premise is proven!

GEM

WHERE'S RONNY?

A scene which could have had a tragic aftermath except for the athletic prowess of the Teeny Tiny Tykey.

My dear ones,

The reason that we were boosting Myrna Lee over the top of a step ladder into our lower bathroom window was because of SILENCE. Anything and everything may, and frequently did happen at River Roost. Everything but silence. When that occurs, something must be wrong! Ronny was missing and the bathroom door was locked on the inside. From the time when they were first invented, bathroom doors have always been locked on the inside, the better to allow little people to flush toilets, turn on faucets, usually with the plug in, play in water and generally have a grand time. Our faucet was running, keeping time with the happy gurgling of two-year-old Ronny. We had begged. We had offered bribes, but the bathroom door remained closed. Ronny was ecstatically happy. So, we pushed Myrna Lee through the window to unlock the door and rescue a little boy who was quite contented not to be rescued at that particular time. He wasn't even hungry and the thing that he wanted less than anything else in the world was to be disturbed while frolicking in the water. For his mother's sake (our dear Aunt Selma, of course), however, we detached the screen and boosted the Tyke through.

Now with that problem solved, I must go.

GEM

LITTLE CHILDREN I REMEMBER

What might have been an interesting dialogue rather than a one-way conversation had I not been mentally confounded and unable to give a plain answer to a simple question.

My dear ones,

Our house was full of "company" when I suddenly felt a most urgent and pressing call of Nature. I quickly reached for my zipper, and since the library bathroom door was ajar, I felt perfectly safe, and walked in. There, on the throne was one of our many little princesses. Dear niece Peggy's four-year-old daughter, precocious Cindy, with her serious adult face and beautiful brown eyes looked up at me and inquired, "Do you have to go to the potty too?"

Then there is this short dissertation on a long reflection:

Whether doing chores or rambling through the woods, Teddy's brother and his sisters found that they could always depend upon him for a quick snack. It seems in retrospect rather odd that this little fellow with his slight frame did not gain in weight unusually fast, because he was forever munching on hidden fruit, crackers or cookies. From his jeans or within his shirt, he was always capable of pulling forth an endless supply of food of some nature, no matter how soiled it might have become. I mention this because my memory has just recaptured the very appropriate name with which Chum had dubbed him: Teddy, the WALKING PICNIC!

And I offer this little weak verse about which I will undoubtedly hear an angry repercussion:

> Myrna Lee
> Did climb a tree.
> She had a stick to boost her.
> But the only thing that she could see
> Was her old Banty Rooster!

> Didn't I warn you?
> GEM

MRS. X

A biography of a lady with unusual and varied talents, about whom much more could be told than will herein be found. I know not why, and sometimes it is better not to ask why, but strict instructions have come down from the highest echelon, my own dear censor, that the dear lady must be designated as Mrs. X only.

My dear ones,

Once a week Mrs. X came to call. Pinned very carefully to her coat with an enormous safety pin was a long list of things about which she didn't fully understand, and which, asking in her broken English, she hoped that Cecile would explain. With nearly fifty years, wealthy in singular experiences, she was still full of old-world mannerisms. Coming from Poland to Chicago as a young woman, she had almost immediately entered into a marriage which had previously been arranged for her, a marriage that was to last for twenty years. Living in that strange, noisy, bustling and frustrating city had not been an altogether happy experience for a girl who loved the soil. She was forty years old when she lost her first husband. Shortly thereafter, she met and married Mr. X, and promptly moved to a twenty-five acre, sandy farm near Hamilton where they operated a small poultry business. Her new husband, physically quite the reverse from his comfortable, round wife, was of Danish descent. He was a slender, dignified, courteous, and immaculately dressed person who always spoke in precise grammar-book English. These two people, so completely different in physical aspects, from the beginning of their marriage, were supremely happy in each other. High in a fire tower overlooking the Allegan State Forest, Mr. X, employed by the conservation department, kept constant watch for any telltale plume of smoke that would indicate the danger of a forest fire.

Because it had been so many years since Mrs. X had been on a farm, and because all phases of farming had experienced an enormous number of changes, she always seemed to have many questions for which she sought an answer. This explains the list which was always pinned to her coat. She never used the names of Cecile or Mrs. McNitt. Her conversation always would begin: "Lady, how about this?" and thus started, she would slowly go down her list of questions. Along with these questions would also come a veritable outpouring from the vast treasury of her memory, a fascinating array of delightfully odd and strangely peculiar information. Her memory was also a repository of "Old World" recipes for delectable dishes, among which was one that she frequently made: a delicious blood sausage, a delicacy of which Chum became inordinately fond.

One very interesting accomplishment, which, under the pledge of secrecy, she taught to a much embarrassed Cecile, was the ability to sex geese. There are supposed to be certain recognizable characteristics in geese, such as the pitch or the shrillness of their voices, or the deepness of the orange color in their bills, which should distinguish between the male and the female, but these characteristics are extremely difficult to recognize. Mrs. X, after several lessons when I was not around, imparted this difficult art to Cecile. Thus it was that my charming wife, with the aid of a jar of Vaseline, became an expert in a very unusual profession, a far cry from being a legal secretary.

Mrs. X would have been horrified at the very thought of panty hose. Her common-sense advice for winter wear was to don "snuggies," long woolen under drawers, a garment which she claimed, not without just cause, was ideally adapted to keep good girls free from wracking coughs and runny noses.

We became accustomed to seeing Mrs. X wearing

her stockings backwards with a worn-out heel on the top of her foot, as a measure of economy dating back to the years when stockings were not available. This seemed rather funny when I first observed this practice, but now, in looking back, I find in this not the slightest bit of humor.

The light sandy soil of their small farm would have defeated most people, but Mrs. X's kitchen garden, amply fertilized with rich chicken droppings, looked like a picture out of a seed catalogue and her flower garden was incomparable. Mr. X, as a fire warden, which took up all of his daylight hours, limited his activities mostly to their small garden, their chickens and their geese. Geese, because of Mrs. X's old world experiences, were her particular pride and joy. She not only could sex them, but what was equally important, she knew how to stuff, or force feed them. She would spend hours going from one goose to another and by holding their bills open, she would literally stuff food down their long necks. The result was not so much a fat goose (although they were that too), but they grew an enormously enlarged liver which became in time another one of her rare delicacies.

I wish that I could end this on a joyful note (and if you, dear reader, want one, you may end the story right here), but that is quite impossible. In the course of time a cancerous growth appeared in the body of Mrs. X. The terrific pain that accompanied this cancer was unbearable. I don't like shocks, but what happened, happened. One evening when Mr. X returned home from his work, he found his wonderful wife and our dear friend hanging woefully in their kitchen.

God rest her soul.

GEM

DIXIE

An attempt to relate in a whimsical fashion an accidental purchase and our life with a considerate friend.

My dear ones,

Although he was blind, he moved with an elegant grace befitting a thoroughbred. When you called, he would lift his head in happy recognition of your voice, and with stately grace he would come carefully, but rapidly, pacing his way toward you with his head held high and his ears pointing sharply upward.

The bidding had been rapid and exciting with many gasps, sighs, ohs and ahs at the auction the day I succumbed to a lifelong desire and bought a horse. At that time we didn't know that he was blind, and some of our neighbors were quite elated and whispered gleefully, "Those McNitts have been took!" If we had stopped bidding at seventy dollars instead of pushing up to seventy-five, one of those same neighbors would have been "took" instead of us, but then that would have been a very different story indeed.

Dixie proved to be, aside from his defect, a very well trained horse, extremely fast, quick to respond to almost any signal and with a sensitive understanding of one's slightest wish. He was brown in color with white stockings and with occasional white patches on his body. Because he was so gentle and kind, everyone immediately fell in love with him. He afforded us all an immense amount of pleasure watching him out in the pasture as he would exercise himself, rhythmically pacing in a circle with the ease and grace which comes only with long practice.

He had an enormous desire for companionship, and he would have liked to have followed the cows when they rambled into the woods nipping at sassafras leaves as they passed, but he soon learned to limit himself to the open fields where there were no obstacles to bump his tender nose.

We soon learned too why it was that we were able to buy such a grand animal so cheap. When we finally did discover his blindness, we were really not as disappointed as we might have been because he so sincerely wanted to please us. Each day, with a twelve-dollar English saddle purchased for us by Count Mischa in former days (we did not feel that we could afford to spend one hundred and fifty dollars for a western saddle), we would saddle Dixie and take our turns in an exciting canter. The tiniest pressure on his neck would be sufficient to turn him in the direction in which one would wish to go. He would also "stop and go" on a simple voice command.

Had any member of my family seen me the day that I was careless and, being in a hurry, neglected to properly tighten the cinch on the saddle, and slipped in a ludicrous half circle, saddle and all, underneath Dixie's body, I most surely would have been the laughingstock of one and all. It was a mark of his excellent training that he came to an immediate stop and waited while I extricated myself from the stirrups. Picking up my gravel-bruised body, I quickly glanced around to see whether anyone was watching my humiliation. If ever a horse had a reason to laugh out loud and tell everyone what had just happened, Dixie certainly did that day!

While everybody had many thrilling hours of enjoyment on Dixie's back, we felt that he should also earn his keep in other ways too. We rigged up a wagon of sorts by converting an old buggy—what a mistake that was! Today, that ancient buggy would be an almost priceless antique. Uncle Ott donated an old harness which today would also rank as an antique, and we hitched Dixie to our makeshift wagon. It was only after much cajoling that we were able to accomplish this feat since our saddle horse had never before been in harness, and he looked with his sightless

211

eyes on our efforts with much disdain. With this conven-ient arrangement, however, we were able to carry down to our range-shelters a daily load of grain for our pullets. We thought that this was a splendid idea, and it was very help-ful as long as we were able to go straight ahead or turn in a large circle; but sadly enough, we never were able to teach Dixie to back up. He might have done so had I been sitting on his back, but of course, I never thought of that. In spite of all the pulling and tugging, shouting and beg-ging, our prize riding horse stood stock still, leaving us to figure some other way out of our foolish predicament: that of getting too close to an immovable object or a too-nar-row passageway. He was a saddle horse and he intended that we should never forget his proper mission in life. When I was silly enough to get into cramped quarters that required such difficult maneuvering that friend Dixie couldn't handle, I unhitched him and with the help of the boys, we would manually back up the wagon, re-hitch our recalcitrant animal and proceed merrily on our way.

More often than not, I would ride our gallant steed "bare-back." Late in the afternoon, I would call to him and he would promptly come running, always glad to be with someone. Rather than to take the time to saddle and bridle him, it seemed easier to grab his mane and swing up on his back and go galloping off after the cows. Returning with them Dixie allowed no laggards. It was genuinely amusing to watch him nudge with his head any cow foolish enough to hesitate in her homeward journey. His sense of smell over-compensated for his lack of sight, and he always knew where his charges were. When he would nudge them, they would jump in a most ungainly fashion. This very important job of "bringing in the cows," had he not been blind, I am sure that he could have done all by himself. Perhaps way up in those beautiful green pastures in the sky, Dixie is even now nudging some wayward cow in her rump and muttering stories about someone who slipped, saddle and all, and tried riding upside down.

The Sage of River Roost will now leave you with this little admonition: never scratch your ear too often when attending an auction sale.

PUPS' TALES AND OUR DEAR UNCLE LEONARD

A frank discussion of (in a back-handed sort of way) my weakness in the face of danger: a back-biting treatise.

My dear ones,

Uncle Leonard's passion for hunting was equaled only by his love of and his loyalty to his dogs—always hounds. The names which he foisted upon them, since for some unknown reason he always named them after the ladies, seemed to put one in mind of some kind, good-natured, rather plump housewife rather than the lean, long animals which were eager and ready for the chase. I recently made some mention of Bessie and rather than leave you with the impression that her occasional tendency to fasten upon the seat of one's pants was her main mission in life, I must tell you that this was not altogether true. She did like to hunt, and if one is to believe the same claim that Uncle Leonard made for all of his dogs, and their names were legion, she was quite good at it. Biting was only a sideline with Bessie and when she indulged herself with this sport, she, differing from Amie, was somewhat tricky. Gazing dreamily into the distance, completely ignoring you, she waited until you felt secure and, still seeming to be looking in the opposite direction, she would quickly attach herself to the back of your lap.

Amie's attitude toward life in general and humans in particular was quite different. She was straightforward; there was no evasion or trickery in Amie. While it is probably true that she was an excellent hunter, her real career, the one to which she devoted herself with an overwhelming happiness, was to frustrate all humans by growling, nipping, and whenever possible, biting them in whatever portion of the body was available. She made no secret of her desire to sink her white teeth into a choice morsel of human flesh. This discussion by no means implies that Uncle Leonard did not take proper precautions with his dogs. Oh, he did! He did! When visiting us he always kept them carefully chained. They were chained either in the back hall, preventing any entrance to the kitchen, or in front of the basement door of the barn, preventing any descent to do chores. Amie, in particular, was always chained, and she guarded the doors near her most assiduously and the only way to gain entrance was to call out for help or, if brave enough, to use a club, a method of persuasion which we never used.

Two or three weeks before we moved from River

Roost and shortly after the death of Amie, a severe blow to Uncle Leonard, for at least to him she had been a long and faithful friend and servant, a friendly, soft-brown-eyed, long eared, small hound of unknown parentage and ownership moved into our yard. Making herself at home, she adopted us. She was a beautiful, gentle, black-and-brown animal who had apparently been brought into our neighborhood and then deserted, a not uncommon practice in our vicinity. Mother and Myrna Lee decided to put her out of the car where Raleigh's shack used to be and then drive rapidly home. This little dog beat them home and was waiting on the back porch with her tail wagging in happy greeting. A few days later the Ludfords came to visit; Uncle Leonard fell in love with her, and naming her Becky, he took her home to train for hunting. Shortly thereafter he was bragging about her ability to flush out and run rabbits in a circle, bringing them back under his gun. True, she ran away at the sound of the shot, but still, he insisted, she was a good hunter and the fact that she was gun-shy made no difference. It has recently come to my attention, however, that he has acquired another dog, a beagle, whom he has named Sam because his father was a "travelin' man." Anyway, he now has two GENTLE dogs and (don't tell Uncle Leonard) but to me, whether or not they can hunt doesn't really matter!

GEM

P.S. A little weak verse to entertain you:

In this History, should you so desire
Are certain truths to which you might aspire.
So, in meekness then, I now inquire,
Is the laborer worthy of his hire?
Credit and where-with-all should never clash
You take the credit and I'll take the cash!

WILD RABBIT DINNER

Relating the dark, dismal failure of a dinner fit for the most discerning gourmet.

My dear ones,

Being, as you know, one who always gives the proper thought to every action, I made my plans well in advance in order to have an excellent dinner all ready for Cecile when she came home from work one night this week. I brought up from our frozen storage a nice little package of what appeared to be a plump wild pheasant and dropped the frozen bundle into a kettle to simmer, visioning in the meantime a delightful and tempting dumpling dish. After the dark meat had thawed and stewed for awhile, I added some onions and carrots; and still later, I added the dumplings so that our meal would be ready at just the proper time. Long since, I have learned not to look a gift horse in the mouth, but this time I wished that I had. I can remember a time in years now long past when we experimented with turtle soup and now I was reminded of that regrettable time. Our partridge turned out to be a wild rabbit which Uncle Leonard had shot while hunting at River Roost and had placed in our freezer where it had been lost and buried under innumerable other packages. Now it was so done that the meat fell off the bones, but like the turtle, the more you chewed the meat, the more like gum it became and so you chewed and chewed and chewed. And the taste—ugh! The fact that it had been frozen for a long time didn't help it any, but also it probably was an old and wise (but not too wise or it wouldn't have been shot), strong, stringy, and tough buck. Of course Uncle Leonard claims that he doesn't sex his rabbits before he shoots them and that, anyway, I should have cooked it in wine. This to me was in the nature of recipes for planked food, where you eat the plank and throw away the food! Anyway I prefer my wine in a thin glass and properly chilled. I was brought up by a father who hunted and expected his family to eat and enjoy his game so perhaps I am prejudiced. Sad to tell, even at home Uncle Leonard is forbidden by wise Aunt Sylvia to put any more wild rabbits in his freezer, and now I know why!

And so with the immortal Will, your reportorial Sage offers this:

Meke less thy body hence, and more thy grace;
Leave gormandizing; know the grave doth gape
For thee thrice wider than for other men.

King Henry IV, Part II (and) GEM

BOW AND ARROWS

A very short article which is worthy of much more space.

My dear ones,

I doubt if ever there was anyone who worked harder at playing with a bow and arrow than did Ted. There was always a bale of straw standing next to the barn which served as a target where Ted and Myrna Lee and several others practiced. When this urge for archery first came upon our children, they began their shooting with small "souvenir," "real Indian" bows, but it was not long before good sturdy long bows appeared. First, they used blunt arrows and as they improved, sharp game arrows came into their quivers, and of course, there was always the general complaint that visiting "little people" would constantly be breaking or losing arrows.

When the river ran high and overflowed the banks, innumerable carp followed the flood to feast on the water -covered grass. As the river receded, the carp became land-locked in the drying pools of water, and here it was that Ted went hunting. He would attach a line to his arrow and let go at the huge carp struggling in the shallow water. They were not too hard to hit, but it was quite a task to

Springtime On The River

pull a twenty-five-or thirty-pound carp sideways through the shallow water and mud. The boys called it sport, but it looks to me like a lot of hard work to acquire some dog or chicken food.

If when you think that this old reprobate
On some occasion seems so much to prate
About your past, that it does complicate
Your happy future with your loving mate,
I'11 change my ways and ask for clemency
If you'll but let me take the currency!

(By golly, I did it again!)
GEM

Summertime On The River

Autumn On The River

Winter On The River

PULLING NAILS

Containing matters military as it affects the chain of command.

My dear ones,

When Uncle Al tore down an old house near his garage (he was an auto and truck mechanic by trade) on Lake Drive in Grand Rapids to make room for a parking lot, he brought out a great deal of used lumber to River Roost. At about the same time Mr. Gitch sold us an old house which the boys helped to tear down, and this old lumber also ended up at the farm. All of this was very valuable material and would have many uses, but first the nails had to be pulled out, not only for safety, but to make it more usable. There is nothing more exasperating than to ruin a good saw blade when trying to cut through an old nail.

Naturally, the job of pulling nails and sorting the lumber was palmed off to the children. Well, not exactly palmed off—as commander-in-chief, or at least a four-star general, I ordered them to get off their duffs and get to work. Following this order, a staff of officers was promptly organized all the way from the top down to the lowly

226

buck privates, who were, of course, Kay and Carol. Chum, Terry, and Ted promptly became the brass, issuing the orders and supervising, but doing little actual work. The children did pull a lot of nails from that lumber that summer but they also learned the military pecking order. "Which is higher, a colonel or a captain? Why can't I speak directly to the captain? I don't want him for my sergeant! How many nails do we have to pull before we can be corporals?" Myrna Lee claims that she was so low that she wasn't even a buck private; a special lower rank was established for her, the wee little private.

"Over the weak shall be set the strong and they shall despoil them!" With that bit of philosophy, I shall pause and reflect a tender moment on man's inhumanity to man.

GEM

TEDDY'S DATE

Relating a curious exchange between a mother and a daughter when the latter attempts to assuage the former.

My dear ones,

When our fifteen-year old-Teddy announced to the family that his buddy Larry had arranged a date for him and that a group of teenagers was going to have a beach party on Lake Michigan's beautiful sandy beach near Saugatuck, the full weight of a mother's worry for her growing son descended full upon me.

"Why," she said, "I don't believe that you have ever had a real father-son talk with Teddy. How do we know what kind of girls will be there? The morals of some of those Chicago girls are not what they might be! Do you think that he should be permitted to go?"

As a matter of fact, I had had several informal talks with both of my sons and I had learned a great many things! As it turned out the girls in question were from a large religious camp, and it seemed that their morals could be vouched for. But Mother continued to worry and incessantly continued to bring up the subject of the coming party until disquieting thoughts began to nag even my complacency. It was a great relief, however, when Kay, who was all of twelve years old at the time, assured us by firmly stating:

"Mother, you don't have to worry. Teddy is much stronger than any of those girls!"

Come then to these silent scenes of peace
Where cares and toil and sadness cease,
Where saint or sage oft does release
A Tale where you may find release.
And thus your efforts, brave and bold
Will give you peace – I'll take the gold!

GEM

MORE CATS

Containing little or nothing, but mostly about cats and more cats.

My dear ones,

If there ever had been a ready market for cat fur, we would have been rich, for that market would have found us with a steady and ever-increasing supply. If there was at any time during our occupancy of River Roost a project upon which we were highly successful, it was the breeding and raising of cats; although, I must admit, it was a project that required no supervision and was quite self-sustaining in all particulars except feeding, at least in part, and we took care of that. A few of these cats were outstanding specimens. Cats like Fluff, Blackie, Mrs. Betts, Boots, Foxy, Puff, and Cleo could easily have been kings and queens in their class and they would undoubtedly have taken first ribbon in any show. But generally our cats were a motley bunch of oddly colored creatures of many hues running anywhere from solid black to solid white with crazy mixtures of yellow, gray, and calico in between. Some came with long hair, some with short; some were handsome animals, some scrawny ones. Toward the end of our stay, due to much inbreeding, there were many of the latter. These cats were the direct result of our theory, "Better to feed cats than rats." In spite of tons and tons of grain and mash that we were constantly feeding all our animals, we were always free of rats, a brag that few of our neighbors could make.

We carried Mrs. Betts with us when we first moved to the farm, an old cat at that time, but she still lived for many years exercising her one great virtue. Twice a year she mated and twice a year she had a single kitten, a prudent self-control never exercised by her progeny, and there were many.

Whenever I went to the barn to do chores, Foxy would land on my shoulders as soon as I entered the door, and he continued to ride there until the chores were done. I was pleased to have him do this in the winter when I was wearing a heavy jacket, but in a light sport shirt this little habit of his was quite trying. His claws were sharp and he hung on with a tenacity that frequently left tiny red beads, particularly so if his initial jump had been a long one and he would land with a thud that would almost bowl me over. But I liked his company. He was loyal and it was pleasant to hear him purring on my shoulder. This habit of jumping to the shoulder, however, was frequently misunderstood by visitors who were often slightly frightened when this large black ball of fur would come flying through the air to land with an unexpected thump on an unresisting body!

Cleo was short for Cleopatra and he was doubly misnamed; it should have been Marc Antony, but actually he was neither a he nor a she, but an IT, since he had been altered before he came to us via Kay after she had married. Cleo had taken a decided dislike to Stan and took up the habit of crouching by the door, the better to bite him when he entered. This was his only antipathy. He was kind and gentle to everyone else, but I guess that Stan tasted better and Cleo couldn't resist a luscious nip whenever possible. He thought that he was a house cat and not properly a barn cat and so he was always waiting by the door to slip in unobserved, or so he hoped. But he was constantly shedding his fur, and when he would rub against and around your legs, he always managed to leave "gobs" of hair on your trousers. For this reason as well as to protect the davenports, he was relegated to the barn, where he was most unhappy. He was never accepted by the other cats and consequently he was always in the position of having to defend himself, leaving him constantly battle-scarred.

Boots also wanted to be a house cat, but he made the mistake of making a mistake while sitting on my lap, and for this reason he also was relegated to the barn where his mistakes wouldn't dampen clothing.

Puff, poor thing, was an unhappy cat. Pure white and long puffy-haired, she was constantly shedding like Cleo, but she also liked to eat birds. After having pounced on Kay's parakeet with grim results followed by copious tears, she also was sent to the barn to live out her many lives, sleeping, dreaming, mousing and mothering with all the other cats. She sure was a pretty one.

There were many times when, I'm afraid, more time was spent in the disenchanting work of attempting to give away our surplus kittens than in the also disenchanting work of providing a livelihood for ourselves as well as our innumerable cats. But on the whole we managed to maintain a reasonable balance between over and under production of our feline population, maintaining a status quo, as it were. Now, years later here on Maple Street, I am down to only one cat, Sabaca, a condition that she seems quite willing to change any day!

"Ignorant people think it's the noise which fighting cats make that is so aggravating but it ain't so; it's the sickening grammar they use" (Mark Twain). But Oliver Herford said, "Cat: a pygmy lion who loves mice, hates dogs, and patronizes human beings."

And so, dear ones, did you say you wanted a kitten?

GEM

GATHERING WOOD

It has been said that the squirrel who spends time gathering and burying acorns in the fall will not be hungry when the snowstorms swirl in the winter; likewise, those who gather wood diligently in the fall will not be chilly in the depths of a Michigan winter.

My dear ones,

For many years when the last leaves fall from the trees and the grass withers and dries; when the cold rain falls almost daily, and daily we expect it to turn to snow, our front porch becomes an object of heated discussion between Cecile and me. And, never in these last few years have her remarks been more pointed or more frowningly directed at me (a poor innocent mortal) than during these last few days.

This year, already 1967 approaches its close, we were going to be independent and not ask, or rather plead with the relatives to help us accumulate firewood for our ravenous fireplace, as they have so kindly done these many, many past years. I bought a special grate with the brilliant idea in mind that we could buy several hundred pounds of anthracite, that is hard coal, which, while hard

235

to ignite is especially clean with little or no smoke and burns for hours and hours with a pleasingly warm and cheerful red glow and leaves very little ash. But, alas, who burns coal in these days of electric and gas heating systems? Some soft coal, mostly in the form of Pocohantas briquettes, was available at the seemingly low price of three fifteen-pound bags for $1.00. We tried them. They were dirty and filthy to handle and were not only smoky, but the odor of its foul gas seeped from the living room throughout the entire house. The three bags lasted one hour!

Merlin, hearing of our plight, came out one Saturday and with the chain saw cut down some dead trees on the edge of the forest and cut them to proper length for our avaricious fireplace. But the weather was miserable and it rained continuously all day in a steady cold drizzle and consequently not too much wood was accumulated. Then Aunt Ruth and Uncle Al, through the bigness of their hearts, came out with the Jeep truck and with the help of your industrious Cecile hauled several large loads of still-usable slab wood from our east field (remnants of our short logging era). With a buzz saw attached to our garden tractor by a V-belt, our porch filled evenly and rapidly with neatly piled rows of wood with more stacked close to the house. It still hadn't snowed and my FATHER decided he must get just as much wood on the porch as possible before any snow came. It is unbelievable! In his pajamas, slippers, and bathrobe flapping around his thin shanks and Ted's old winter cap on his head, all 100 pounds and eighty-four years of him set to work like a beaver. Tugging, piling, and throwing, he has completely filled our porch until wood actually touches the porch ceiling! I sit here now with bated breath and look out, expecting any minute to see and hear a piece come sliding down and go crashing through one of the living room windows. Each night dear Cecile takes another look, turns slightly pale, and muttering under her breath, glances at me and stalks out to the kitchen. Such mutterings as: "Can't even see the road....It's like living in a fort—I'll get claustrophobia." I gather that she is trying to tell me that something must be done because the whole front view is completely blocked, and she knows that a heavy wind could very easily blow some of it and send it smashing through the window, and then the window would have to be taken into the lumber yard for new glass while the cold winds blow throughout the house. I love the warmth and comfort of our fireplace, but even I am awed by that huge pile of wood.

Well, Dad beat the snow; so go out on the porch

and get a piece of wood for the fire; actually, get a whole armful while you're out there, would you? Then we could sit by the warm fire and you could tell me a tale.

GEM

TED'S UNDERWEAR

This is a portion of our life wherein Ted discovers some harsh facts of life and thus finds that clothes DO make the man!

My dear ones,

It is a tragedy in the ruthless advance of civilization that the day when "long-handled" woolen underwear hung frozen and stiff as a board from the clothesline no longer exists in the memories of most of us. We have exchanged the warmth and itchy comfort of 100% woolen underwear for abbreviated shorts and sleazy undershirts and for the dubious privilege of shivering, chattering, and catching cold in our race to be "modern."

Ted had never known the comforting warmth of this sensible garment, which had many built-in features of uncommon convenience. This item of an almost sensuous luxury has long since disappeared from merchants' shelves. The poor boy never knew that such a garment had ever existed. During his Christmas holidays while he was on vacation from school, an opportunity presented itself for him to earn extra pocket money. Ted found that, when working for Uncle Al in his auto repair shop, it often became necessary to lie full length under a car on the concrete floor of the garage where doors constantly opened to allow blasts of wintry air to flood over him. It was then that he discovered that something, he knew not what, was missing from his attire. Anything warmer than what he was now wearing would do.

Nothing is ever thrown away at River Roost. Closets and the drawers of a bureau, a chest, or a cupboard contain everything from a pair of broken shears to a piece of twine or a burnt-out fuse, old flashlight batteries, left-hand gloves, small tools, nails, wrapping paper, etc., etc., and discarded underwear. It was no problem for Mother to rummage through these drawers and come up with a pair of Grandpa's discontinued long-handled underwear. This piece of apparel was accepted by Ted and in grateful wonder he struggled into them. He found that while they were indeed warm, they were also a trifle uncomfortable. All day he fussed with the too-long sleeves which constantly kept creeping down over his hands. He further wondered why there should be in this garment a long horizontal slit which opened on his chest. When he took this underwear off after his first day of wear, he studied them closely, arranging and rearranging this most recalcitrant piece of clothing. Finally his mother, that great seer and most knowledgeable of persons, explained that for comfort clothes of any kind should never be worn upside down!

At our annual Christmas party for the family where everyone was expected to furnish a share of the entertainment, Aunt Sylvia, amongst much boisterous advice and with many sly innuendoes, performed for our enlightenment with much grace and charm both the right way and the wrong way of putting on "long-handles." The raucous laughter which accompanied her antics left our Teddy very red-faced indeed!

A NEWS FLASH: FREEDOM OF THE PRESS DENIED!

I also wrote this day a thoughtful essay on the mores of our generation, but unfortunately it is now in the hands of the censor. The world has long awaited this forward step in literature. Write to your congressman (Cecile) and get a release for this monumental work.
FURTHER NOTE: It isn't really all that bad, but when pressure from the head office is brought to bear, well–

My love,

GEM

MY *TRUE* MAGAZINE

A letter which was roughed out to be sent to you some time ago was somehow relegated to my file of notes and I do not think that it was ever sent out. At least, I don't think that it was, because the little lady (Cecile, of course), who has always been most ready with her kind suggestions, suggested that I should not send it! But now it has been just released by the "censor."

My dear ones,

Among other magazines, when the high school youngsters put on their annual money making drive, we always subscribed to *True–The Man's Magazine*. This year was no exception, but somehow our order was fouled up and when my first issue was delivered, it was *True Story*, and not just plain *TRUE*!

The titles of the various stories in this strange magazine were not only beguiling, but were also a fine example of that illusionary art of misdirection, for they never, never fulfilled their promises of fascinating reading. Titles such as: "MY HUSBAND AND I ARE WHITE, (but our baby is black!," "LOVE IN A ROW BOAT, (it was either that or drown!)," "THE MAN I MARRIED IS

ONLY 15 YEARS OLD!""I SPENT MY WEDDING NIGHT WITH A STRANGER!," "I AM MARRIED TO MY OWN BROTHER," "MY HUSBAND PAID MY DOCTOR TO TRICK ME INTO PREGNANCY," "I LET MY FATHER-IN-LAW LOVE ME, (but my husband is to blame)." There are articles like "I NEED A MAN, NOT A MOUSE" or "MISTAKEN FOR A CALL GIRL," and finally, "MY MOTHER MAKES ME TAKE BIRTH CONTROL PILLS." Such so-called stories would tend to make one wonder how much one has missed in all his years of courageous reading. Actually, these stories really do not measure up to their inviting titles. They leave you with a letdown feeling, rather like listening to the 'shill' (the pitch man!) at a carnival and then discovering that the whiskers on the "dog-faced" boy are false. Example? "MY HUSBAND AND I ARE WHITE, (but our baby is black!)" The baby was black, but he was adopted! Etc., etc., false conclusions all!

The advertising in this magazine is a little more likely to pique your interest. An advertisement on one page tells how to increase your bust line while on another page an ad inquires, "Do you desire to decrease your bust line?" (Money back guarantee too). For only $14.95 one can purchase a permanent hair remover for "that unwanted hair." "Too skinny?" "Secret loans." "Play the guitar in 7 days." "Kiss and cry no more!" "The illustrated encyclopedia of sex for only $2.95"(a complete doctor's guide in a plain wrapper.) Somebody has a "cure" for every perceived human malady, and don't forget to send in lots of money too!

I recently received a letter from the high school telling me that a correction has been made in my subscription and that I will soon be receiving *TRUE* again.

In the last issue of *True Story* there was an advertisement for a magazine of the same ilk, *True Confessions*, where in the next issue I notice that I can learn how "MY SISTER AND I SHARE ONE HUSBAND," "A PASSION GREATER THAN THE LAW MADE US DO IT," "MY DOCTOR MADE ME STERILE, (but I didn't know it!)," "THE SLEEP-WALKING BRIDE (I woke up in a stranger's arms!)." It would certainly look like the old merry-go-round extends also to other magazines.

While awaiting a release from the censor for this essay, my *TRUE* magazine has started to come through the mail again quite regularly, but so also, after three years, does *True Story*! While we no longer suffer the disappointment which comes from actually reading the stories, there is still a mad rush to grab this innocuous pulp magazine in order to scan all the intriguing titles!

No small wonder that a day's work of this nature is very tiring. It will sure feel good to lie down for a while. Hand me that magazine over there, would you please?

GEM

CHUM'S GRADUATION

My dear ones,

    Proving that I alone do not write all of this "Historie" as is witnessed by this copy of an ancient and barely legible manuscript, I discovered a paper buried beneath ageless mounds of documents during our recent removal from River Roost. It was written for an English class by that Teeny-Tiny-Tikey (Myrna Lee), and it even has a teacher note "good" with a mark of *A*.

    One of the clearest memories I have of my brother's high school was his graduation from Zeeland High. Actually the event which was so memorable was not the genuine graduation itself but a small ceremony which took place on our farm.

    As it happens at any family event, all of the relatives had congregated in a somewhat sedate throng, waiting with anticipation to leave for the auditorium for the exercises. My mother, rather nervous with the aspect of having her eldest child graduate, was scurrying about putting the finishing touches on my brother and the rest of us. Finally, completely ready, my brother had donned his royal-blue robe and mortarboard and was waiting with his siblings for our parents to leave for Zeeland.

I have a cousin who places a great deal of value on tradition, and so feeling that this was a milestone in my older brother's life, since he would soon leave the farm for college, Merlin firmly believed that my older brother in a respectable ceremony should pass his farm responsibilities to his younger brother. So, Chum, decked in "cap and gown" and Ted, my other brother, in a fancy grey suit, were led by my cousin to the back of the barn. Then eldest brother with a magnificent flourish presented his next of kin with his pitch fork, a tool with which he had spent many a "happy hour." My cousin, realizing the levity of the situation, took with him a camera to preserve for posterity this colorful event for my unknowing mother who would have fainted if she had known—and when the pictures were processed, she did!

Myrna Lee

BUCKY

A surprising and embarrassing situation which developed in the course of a ride out to River Roost.

My dear ones,

About the middle of our occupancy of River Roost we again approached a problem which was to renew itself and frequently came to plague us. The danger of constant inbreeding with the resulting deterioration of quality within our flock of sheep necessitated occasionally changing the buck which was to sire our lambs, and this was one of those occasions. Fortunately, this situation arose at the same time that the Ludfords decided to eliminate their flock. And so the following, in Uncle Leonard's own inimical way, is the tale of his experience when he delivered Bucky to us:

"Fill 'r up," I said to the young fellow at the gas station. He bent to insert the nozzle in the gas tank of my car and came eyeball to eyeball with old Bucky, my pet ram sheep that I had in the back seat. With his long wool mutton-chop whiskers, bushy eyebrows, black nose and large grey eyes, he was calmly looking out the side window. Cars were nothing new to him as he had been carted around to other farms on previous occasions in a similar fashion.

I was taking him out to Uncle Glenn's farm near Hamilton to start a new dynasty in his declining years. Since he was a pet who ate out of my hand every morning, I couldn't serve him up on the table to the family for dinner in good conscience. He was too old to sell. What else was I to do with old Bucky? So I was glad I had found a new home for him at River Roost; he could spend his last years doing what he enjoyed most.

Each time the young gas station attendant's head would come up, he found old Bucky, from a distance of about six inches staring at him with an unblinking gaze. Each time he would quickly avert his eyes in an effort not to appear rude. After this had happened several times, the young man was getting more and more curious. I finally said, "That is an old buck sheep I am taking out to a new farm."

A light seemed to dawn in the young man's eyes as he quickly turned to me with a grin. "Oh, my! I thought he was your grandfather!" he said. Oh, my, indeed!

Uncle Leonard

As the faithful sun sinks slowly over the horizon of Lake Michigan, I beg your indulgence until I can insert a new sheet in the old typewriter.

"It is man that makes Truth great, and not Truth that makes man great." So said Confucius and I echo the same.

GEM

RASCAL AND THE RACCOONS

A whimsical adventure of a man, a boy, a dog, and a gun, and also the telling of a peculiar method of harvesting.

My dear ones,

I often used to say that Rascal was the world's only laughing dog. Not that he was particularly loud when he laughed, but when he was happy, especially when seeing a member of the family after a long absence, he would stretch his lips to their fullest extent, exposing his teeth, and emit a low throaty gurgle. He made a most ludicrous appearance when he would try to wriggle the rear portion of his body at the same time that he was stretching his lips in his grinning laugh.

The year that we raised ten thousand white leghorn pullets on contract for sale at the "ready-to-lay stage," usually about twenty weeks of age, Rascal was unusually helpful to us. At the first sign of evening, we would go down on the range to close up the shelters for the night against the depredations of the raccoons who were masters of the art of opening, with their clever fingers, the simple latches which were ordinarily used to close up the shelters. We had to use something more secure, like a padlock. Our flock of leghorns somehow felt that they should roost in

251

the nearby trees rather than trust to the security of the comfortable roosts within the shelters. Each evening it became necessary for us to harvest our "leghorn trees" as I waggishly called the pine, the oak, and the elm trees which filled up with our recalcitrant leghorns every night. This became a time-consuming task and it was usually quite dark before we finally chased the final chicken down from the trees. It was never too dark for Rascal. He would locate even the most distant trees which had filled up with leghorns roosting in their branches, and standing at the base of the tree he would bark constantly until we came to chase the pullets out of the tree with the use of long sticks or manually shaking the slimmer trees. As soon as the birds would fly down from their forbidden perch, Rascal would promptly chase them back to their proper shelter, sometimes returning to us, smiling with a mouthful of feathers.

Answering Rascal's call one evening, we discovered that it was not a chicken roosting up on dark branches which had captured his attention, but instead four young raccoons had sought safety in the thick branches and stared down at us with baleful eyes. What to do? What to do? Eddie, our dear Aunt Ruth's eldest, was recuperating from a badly infected foot which had resulted from stepping on a rusty nail while helping his father, Uncle Al to all of us, tear down an old house on Lake Drive in Grand Rapids to make room for more parking. Anyway, he was staying with us at that time. I let out a tremendous bellow, calling for Eddie to come down to the range and to bring a gun with him. Along with my bellowing and Rascal's barking, Eddie finally heard me. He soon appeared out of the gloom of early dusk, hobbling and jumping painfully on one foot, but carrying that all-important gun. Unfortunately, however, he had brought along only two shells and we were facing four raccoons. Nevertheless, he angled himself around in such a position that he was able to get two coons within the sight of his gun. His two shells, coupled with an unusual aim, resulted in releasing us from the depredations of at least three of these chicken-loving, thieving critters. The droll appearance of that slender youth staggering down the hill toward me in what must have been a very distressing effort was memorable. It is easy, I suppose, to laugh on such an occasion, but there was also something admirable in this dissociation between what was most comfortable and what was a very helpful act. With both Rascal and Eddie to help, what more could I ask?

GEM

A PEACOCK AND AN OPOSSUM

A curious paragraph or two concerning a frightful, toothy animal with a long and ratty tail which so frightened Cecile that she called for help from your worthy and brave historian.

My dear ones,

Near the apple trees which I have previously discussed was a small shelter which was formerly the home of many consecutive flocks of baby chicks, but which for the last two years has housed Uncle Al's lonesome but beautiful peacock who came to live at River Roost because his plaintive and repeated call so annoyed one of Aunt Ruth's neighbors that he threatened to file suit unless he was relieved from that high-pitched raucous shriek. As the result of Aunt Ruth's ultimatum, Pedro now lives a lonely existence in our brooder house which opens on a reasonably large fenced-in area sufficient enough for short strolls. Down in my heart I believe that Pedro has only been calling for a mate, and I have been trying to induce Uncle Al to purchase a female companion for him.

Recently I took out to him four hamburg buns which he is most found of, tearing them to shreds with his sharp bill before devouring them. His house, however, and this was unusual, was quite devoid of any other food, particularly corn, which was second on his menu. Not wanting to make another trip (I had already done more walking that day than I should have), I waited until Cecile came home and then asked her if she would be kind enough to take a few ears of corn out to Pedro. She, of course, acceded to my request and went trudging through the snow towards Pedro's home. My aching back, however, was not to be favored that day, for Cecile returned to the house on a run and breathlessly informed me that my help was urgently needed. Armed with an ax and Cecile carrying a ball bat, we marched back to the brooder house. I opened the door and peering in, I saw two beady eyes watching me over a metal feed tray. An opposum had been enjoying Pedro's food, for I don't know how long, and now he was warily watching me. He must have realized that his position was quite vulnerable, for he immediately curled up into a ball and pretended to be dead. However, with my ax, I advanced valiantly into battle and quickly disposed of this intruder, which I then offered to Skippy, who ignored him and trotted safely back to his dog house. I limped back to my davenport.

GEM

Old Tree

WHAT DO THOSE AMATEURS KNOW?

My dear ones,

You should see our basement! Or at least a portion of it—that part which first comes into view when you make the last turn in your descent. Myrna Lee and her Uncle Al have gone into the greenhouse business, not, of course, for a profit (whatever that may be), but that type of 'green thumb' thing which permits the grower to scatter black dirt in profusion wildly in every direction. Since most greenhouses are built on dirt floors, these budding agriculturists think that this is true of our basement and they have forgotten such a commonplace tool as a broom. Under fluorescent lighting they have boldly taken over the laundry room; and by pushing two large tables together and placing thereon 'flat' after 'flat' of soil especially treated with their own formula, they have planted them with, literally, thousands of seedlings! My carefully calculated bet would be that there are a minimum of 300 broccoli plants alone, shooting up their green heads and along with countless other plants ranging from beets (why beets?) to zinnias, all begging for water. Little sticks, the kind that

Seedlings

you stir a commercial plastic cup of coffee with, mark each kind of plant, and believe me, there are a lot of sticks in use! Aunt Ruth has already issued a directive: "If you plant it, you process it." Where in the wide world they expect to plant all of these little green things remains a complete mystery to me; especially is this true of ML, who at the very best is limited to a border along the driveway and about six inches close to the house.

Imagine, if you will, my baffled surprise yesterday, when a large dump truck drove into the driveway and a tall driver came knocking on our back door, arousing Sandy, our usually friendly cocker spaniel, into a frenzy. He inquired, "Where do you want me to dump this load of black dirt?" I scratched my ever-thinning hair while he added, "It must have been your daughter who ordered it." I could think of no place better than the driveway, and that is where that huge pile now stands; but my daughter assured me that she had "lots of places to put it." In ML's senior year at college she took a course in horticulture, and in every window or corner of the house there already stands or hangs evidence of her handicraft. This is all very beautiful and very interesting until one encounters the ladybugs crawling down the wall in search of some new plant where there might be more aphids to feed upon. ML just grinned about this incursion of these gentle and help-ful ladybugs until one decided to take a shower with her. The house still reverberates with her shrill screams!

Besides the major gardening project that she has

going in the basement, ML has also been very busy, and probably I should say successfully busy, working with a youth group at our church. One of the many projects which she encouraged her young people to do was the making of religious posters. The day that she came home with a complete kit of tempera water colors, I grabbed a brush and permitted my uncontrolled hand to run wild in brushing out an extravaganza of brilliant colors which I justified, as do most so-called modern impressionists, by drawing attention to my masterful, commanding strokes; but everybody just laughed and called my attempt at art a mess.

What do those amateurs know?
GEM

SHIRT ON THE LINE

In which, while airing our linen, the "tale" of a shirt becomes more and more involved.

My dear ones,

Mother, wearing her dictator's mantle, watched skeptically from the kitchen window while Chum and Ted took turns mowing the lawn with our five-horsepower garden tractor. She had just hung a basket of laundry on the line to dry in the warm sun. The boys, mowing around that laundry, weren't cutting the grass close enough to the poles to satisfy her constant desire for perfection in all things, and so it was that she suddenly rushed outdoors, shouting, "Hold everything! I'll show you just how it should be done." At the very moment when she captured control of the tractor, a short gust of wind caught hold of a wet sport shirt hanging from the line and wrapped it around the handle of the moving tractor, which, of course, pulled it from the security of the wooden pins. It continued its sloppy, flapping, downward movement until it became entangled with the chain drive of the tractor and was systematically and thoroughly ripped into shreds. This sport shirt, an expensive one, might have been Chum's. It might have been Ted's. It might even have been mine. It wasn't. The previous day Chum had been sailboating with one of his more affluent high school friends, and due to the high winds and the consequently high waves, he had received a most thorough soaking. His friend's mother had insisted on loaning him a dry outfit, including the sport shirt (her husband's) which was now completely in shreds. Mother, grim of visage alongside the hidden grins of her sons, stopped in the middle of her work and drove fifteen miles to Holland to purchase a new shirt, which she then delivered to the mother of Chum's friend with appropriate apologies.

Two or three years after the above sad event, a male chorus was touring Michigan presenting concerts for the benefit of our church, and it became our obligation to open a home for two of the boys. One of the boys had forgotten to bring his dress shirt and had been wearing an extra one, which he had borrowed from one of his friends. After several wearings this shirt was badly in need of laundering, which my ever-indulging wife offered to do. The following morning, a Sunday, I was up early and finding that the shirt was not yet dry, I brilliantly attempted to iron it dry. Yes, wouldn't you know it; the shirt was made of synthetic fibers, which promptly melted under the hot iron. So, again the McNitts bought another new shirt. Good deeds are often expensive!

"How far that candle throws his beam! So shines a good deed in a naughty world." William Shakespeare for
GEM

Shirt on The Line

263

VASES

When a house contains many varieties of one item, a discussion arises as to the purpose for the many varieties of the same: I think it is high time that I talk about vases.

My dear ones,

In our house there are many vases; I am speaking of those that should be used for floral arrangements, from small bud vases to medium vases which could be used for large bouquets. We don't have vast urns, but rather the dainty and attractive vases which are scattered in profusion all over our house. There are vases on the piano, on the buffet, on the china cabinet, on the refrigerator in the pantry, on the refrigerator in the kitchen, on window ledges and bookshelves in several rooms. In fact, wherever there is the remotest possibility of placing a vase, there you will find one! I became aware of these vases recently while dusting (yes, I was really dusting!) for Cecile. Our vases, however, are not used for flowers. Oh, no! That would be quite impossible, as you will perceive because they are used as depositories. In their hollow interiors you will find letters, yellow with age, postage stamps without any "stickum" on the back, and occasionally, but just occasionally,

Vases

good stamps. You will also find crayons, rubber bands, paper clips, bobby pins, hair pins, safety pins and peacock feathers. You will find screws, regular pins, buttons, nails, tacks, stubs of pencils and stray pennies. You will find erasers that don't erase, and ball point pens that don't or won't write. You will also find keys. In one vase I found and counted one hundred and twelve keys. Cecile doesn't want them thrown out because they might fit "something, someday!" One large vase was filled with long out-of-date coupons, hundreds of them. There also were two unsigned report cards carefully hidden in one!

Now you know what happens to those little things which are lying around when it is time to pick it all up and clean house. How many vases do you have in your house, huh? I'll understand if you want to go have a little peek.

GEM

PHEASANTS

Touching with no little nostalgia on matters relating to man's inhumanity to man and to the creatures under his dominion, this, our nostalgia, has now become a state of concerned anger.

My dear ones,

One of the few game birds comparable to the wild Canada geese for their exquisite natural beauty is the Chinese pheasant, which was introduced into this country many years ago to satisfy that special yearning of the hunter for an exciting sport which at the same time yielded a most succulent and satisfying repast. A cock pheasant in full flight, soaring only six to ten feet above the ground, his beautiful array of colors easily discernible at such a low height, is thrilling for anyone fortunate enough to behold him. Like a domestic chicken, and similar in weight to the lighter breeds, he prefers to walk unless excited or disturbed. When in flight, however, his soaring, graceful, and vivid beauty is a masterpiece of Mother Nature's art. The pheasant has thrived in this country, perhaps even more so than in its native land. This is particularly true in the midwestern or "corn belt" and adjacent grain states. Fall cornfields have indeed become a source of pleasure for a man and his dog; at least this was true in the early years at River Roost. In many instances the farmer actually reaps a harvest from the sport more golden than the corn which the pheasants assist him in harvesting.

The female pheasant is rigidly protected by law and she seems to know this. It is no uncommon sight to see a string of previously anxious and hurried motorists wait patiently and admiringly while mama pheasant cautiously leads her brood across the highway. Our neighborhood was very fortunate in its pheasant population, and driving into church on a Sunday morning, we often vied with one another to see who could count the largest flock.

This delightful game has now faded into history, for the sight of a pheasant these days is the exception and not the rule. Pollution of air and water as well as the vast amounts of insecticides used by farmers in recent years have taken their toll on our pheasant population. The sport of hunting these fine birds is now but a fond memory.

Now, after baby-sitting on a Saturday night, we take Kimmy and Michael to Sunday School and as we drive along we can only say, "On this strip of road, we once could see–!"

"What is a pheasant, Grandpa?"
GEM

GOOSE DOWN AND A PILLOW

How the down from a goose became the pillow for my head.

My dear ones,

Uncle Sam was not the only person, symbolic or human, who operated a draft. Thus it was that Cecile drafted me for an extremely sneezy job. Down to the basement she led me, if not by the nose, it was certainly by insidious guile. "Just for a few minutes," she said. "Hold these new pillow cases while I transfer and add some new down to them." I did. She did. After the transfer, which had been made necessary because the old cases had developed "leaks" and were losing their resiliency, I had been promised I know not what, but I do know that I yielded with my accustomed good grace! The pillows had to be reconditioned by the addition of new down from Cecile's inexhaustible sack which came into being way back when we were raising geese. At the time of this adventure I was wearing a dark wool jacket and dark slacks, and by the time that the job was completed I had become in truth, "Frosty, the Snowman." Covered I was, from head to foot with white down. Down in my hair, down in my eyebrows, and not only in, but up my nose. The stuff was alive! Wherever it touched me, it clung with a tenacity that only a leech could duplicate. To bring me back to any semblance of a human, Cecile, giggling at the sight of me, had to use the heavy-duty vacuum cleaner with its enormous sucking power. It did get rid of most of the down and even almost sucked me into the hose. But, we do have two "just-like-new" pillows. Oh, yes, there is still down in the sack!

Now I lay me down to sleep,
GEM

THE BORROWED LADDER

"Neither a borrower nor a lender be."

My dear ones,

The importance of certain tools becomes more apparent when the need arises and the needed item is not at hand. When we first went to River Roost to live, we discovered how badly we would need one. Rather than buy one, we yielded to the urging of one of our good neighbors and borrowed one, a thirty-two foot ladder, two sixteen-foot extensions. The first time that we extended it up against the house, it fell and a goodly portion was broken, much to our dismay. Into Hamilton we went and did that which we should have done in the first place; bought a new extension ladder, which we gave to our neighbor, keeping the broken one for our own use. Thus it was that we ended up with a sawed-off twenty-nine footer which was just sufficiently short to make us realize, every time we went to use it, the importance of the longer ladder, and the importance of NOT being a BORROWER ! Not that all of this verbosity is necessarily of any great interest or is particularly amusing, nor was it written to point to the opening admonition, but rather to give a glimpse of one more

271

of the many frustrations that made life at River Roost more interesting.

And that is why, although we bought a longer ladder, we use a shorter ladder.

GEM

DISHES

A pernicious way of speaking that could easily lead to a serious misunderstanding between two otherwise most agreeable people.

My dear ones,

    I always secretly took exception with my wife when she would calmly, but with token sincerity, state: "We won't bother with the dishes now. There are only a few, and we will do them later." LATER! This word was always used in the most disparaging way with an absolute disregard to the actual existing quantities, and there were usually mountains of dishes to be manhandled in some way or other, that the average guest would take Cecile at her word and would drop listlessly into the nearest and most comfortable chair. Or, just as frequently, they would not even use enough energy to drag themselves away from the table.

    Now, I will leave this matter to you who the "we'll do them later," actually was. By the time the guests had finally departed and the children had long since been securely tucked into bed, I was just plain "stuck!" It is facetious statements like the one my wife so often used that try men's souls!

        "Only a few" she said.

                GEM

PIGLETS AND KITTENS

A curious page or two which could not exactly be called a panegyric on pigs.

My dear ones,

Not wishing to miss a single opportunity to start a golden stream flowing into our treasure chest, we decided that we should not waste a moment getting into the profitable pig business. It was inevitable that we would attend the first farm auction that offered hogs for sale. It was also inevitable that we yielded in our naive innocence to the fast-talking, wise-cracking auctioneer. To the great delight of my sons, who were with me, and to the despair of their mother, who was not, I waved my hand wildly at the raucous gibberish of that auctioneer, and so I bought two "bred" young sows guaranteed to farrow in two or three weeks. At the end of two months we still had no new little piglets. Figuring that we had "been had," we sold one of the sows to Uncle Ed and trucked the other one to a neighboring boar to have the job done, which in our ignorance we supposed had already been done. With a patience that we were rapidly learning to exercise, we awaited the necessary one hundred and ten days to elapse by feverishly studying the current farm journals wherein we learned all the latest scientific methods of raising pigs.

First, it seemed, one must build a farrowing pen,

small, but of a size that would permit the mother ample room to move around. It needed a bottom board of one side just high enough for the baby pigs to move at will into a neighboring pen, thus preventing the mother from inadvertently lying upon her newborn infants. The adjoining pen was also small, but it did have a heat lamp hanging in one corner to provide warmth and comfort for those little animals which, according to the journals, should grow into one hundred eighty or two-hundred-pound hogs in five months. Properly fed with all necessary minerals and vitamins, they could, of course, be bigger than that.

All in proper time our sow did indeed bring into the world ten little squeaking bits of perpetual hunger. But in spite of the near-zero February weather, they completely ignored the heat lamp for the comforting warmth of their mother. The necessity of competing for one of only eight faucets for ten hungry mouths kept them close to her as well.

Science was not wasted, however. Under the warm rays of the heat lamp, our barn cat gave birth to six scrawny kittens, which were bothered not at all by the pigs, and they all lived to a ripe old age.

We always did extremely well in the kitten department!

GEM

FIFTEEN MINUTE CLOCKS
AND LOCKED DOORS

Containing a short scene of major distress with comments on the consequences of being too careful.

My dear ones,

Always there were certain things that had to be done Mother's way, and any amount of cajoling wouldn't change her habits. The clock had to be set fifteen minutes fast on the futile theory that if it were fast, little people would get to places, like school, for instance, on time. I tried to tell her that since they all knew that the clock was set fast, these little people would just set their minds to the correct time and so her changing of the clocks was just so much balderdash. Thus explains why the kitchen clock at the Roost was always running fifteen minutes ahead of the rest of the world all the years we lived on the farm.

She also insisted on locking all doors, and in many cases, doubly locking them. She would lock the kitchen door after she had also locked the screen door. This meant that even if you had a key, it would do you no good unless you cut a hole in the screen door, reached in and unlatched it before trying your key. Late on one Fourth of

July night I had to protect Cecile, or so I thought, because of suspicious sounds from burglars who were attempting to gain entrance to the house. Stumbling downstairs, half awake, I was just in time to help Teddy, who was bellying his way through the library window after removing the screen and forcing up the sash. In order to do this, he had to take a precarious position on top of the porch swing and by maintaining just the correct balance, he was able to remove the screen. Halfway through the window, with his feet waving wildly in the air, the sash fell and pinned our boy in the rather ridiculous position of a swimmer in mid-air.

It seems that all the world plays a waiting game
For Fate to make a record of our fame;
For fun, for money or marbles, your name
Will here be inscribed and I'll share the blame.
But since all history can't be funny,
Then you take the marbles, I'll take the money!
What time is it anyway?
GEM

RALEIGH

In which this Historie turns back in order to introduce you to a man whom we first met on our first visit to River Roost.

My dear ones,

When Mischa Thorgevsky was not hunting or otherwise engaged at River Roost, he left the property in the charge of his caretaker, Mr. Raleigh Greenault. Perhaps not everyone in Allegan County knew Raleigh, but certainly at one time or another, they had heard of him. "Sure, I know who you mean. He's that old drunken 'coot' that lives in a shack on the banks of the Kalamazoo River." This, conceivably, is rather an unfair description, but one that was too often used. Those people who knew Raleigh and could call him friend, and they were legion, had a feeling for him that could more aptly be described as a benevolent fondness. Always thoughtful of others, never thoughtless, Raleigh was his own worst enemy, a weak man, but a gentle man, never imposing, but often imposed upon.

He early and easily excused himself from the responsibilities of marriage and of his family with an amiable unconcern which, understanding his lackadaisical character, seemed altogether fitting and proper.

He was always, it seemed, giving something away. This was so because someone was always giving him something, which he then passed on to others casually, with a most natural unconcern for the morrow. A gift from a farmer of a dozen heads of cabbage meant to Raleigh a dozen calls in his decrepit Chevy in order to distribute them to others. When the commercial fishing tug, the owners of which were Raleigh's hunting buddies, mostly out of season, returned to Saugatuck with a good catch, they would often give him a hundred pounds or so of perch, which he would promptly divide with twenty-five or thirty different families in his neighborhood. The mystery in all of this was how in the world he could keep gas in his ancient car. This bounty which he received went on the year around, not only during the harvest season, but also during the hunting season, legal or not. Pheasant, squirrel, duck, geese, rabbit, and venison were always being parceled out to his friends. On one occasion, when the son of our congressman was well "in his cups" and raided his father's freezer, the result of that raid, expensive steaks and roasts, was also distributed. In addition, there were also all those unwanted pups and kittens for which he always seemed to be able to find a home. His personal needs were few and so he kept but little out of the many gifts which were given to him.

"Too bad he drinks; he's a swell guy." He did drink continuously and perhaps by certain standards excessively, but he seemed to be that rare kind of individual upon whom alcohol had little noticeable effect. He never drank alone, whether this was by choice or because he was seldom alone is debatable. He always had drinking companions, brothers of the brush (hunting partners), or, as was often the case, some of Holland's leading industrial executives, who chose his shack for their secret bouts of conviviality. On our first New Year's Day at River Roost, we held an "open house," and of course, Raleigh came. This was one occasion when perhaps he did overindulge. He made his jumbled farewells and started his car to drive the half mile to his home. It was then that, instead of driving home, he started a continuous circuit of our house, out one driveway and into the other; around and around he went, with the entire household gathered at the many windows to watch his erratic encirclement of our house. An awareness of what he was doing finally must have come to him and he straightened out his car into the road and started westward, a direction which he continued for four dred feet, when he then pulled up to the side of the road and fell asleep.

During the heyday of Saugatuck and of Raleigh, that period when he lived with his family, Saugatuck was the favorite vacation spot for the wealthy good guys with their expensive yachts. It was also a favorite spot for the bad guys, Chicago's bootlegging gangsters in their expensive, shiny, black, bullet-proof cars, who roared up Lake Michigan's shoreline to enjoy an outing not too far from their important businesses. Raleigh was the owner and pilot of a side-wheel river boat which carried joy riders from Saugatuck to New Richmond and back. Prosperity and regular employment, however, were not for him and he soon gave up his business and, so to speak, retired.

After his boating venture went the way of all seasonal and often absentee mismanagement, Raleigh took up his residence along the banks of the beautiful Kalamazoo River ,where he trapped, hunted in and out of season, and entertained his friends and inevitably his friends' friends. Long before he was affluent enough to own the tiny shack which was located at the edge of a twenty-acre tract of land bordering River Roost, but was actually situated smack in the center of the county road, he lived in a tent. After Raleigh spent a precarious and

281

excessively cold existence under canvas, someone gave him the small building, which he prevailed upon one of his many friends to jack up onto a truck and to haul to the location next to our property, or more accurately at that time, Mischa's property.

Conservation laws were not made for Raleigh. He knew every foot of the wild and tangled wilderness along the Kalamazoo. After driving down a point for a well just a few feet, he found good water, and so, along with his bird dog, he lived a contentedly lazy life. Oh, yes, he had a dog, a gift from a friend, a splendid animal, and an expensive animal, who proved his value as a bird dog the day that he ran away and sauntered into our yard and playfully killed over one hundred baby chicks. Raleigh was extremely sorry about this and he apologized most profusely, promising to repay us for our loss just as soon as he got paid by a neighbor whom he had helped at harvest time. My guess is that he never got paid; we never did either...

Although it was only one hundred and fifty miles from Chicago, the whole area, running anywhere from five to fifteen miles on either side of the Kalamazoo River from Allegan to Saugatuck, was an unbelievable and almost impenetrable jungle of marshes, bayous, draining swamps, and spring-fed creeks. It was a section of awesome wild beauty in every season, located in that southern portion of West Michigan which also harbored a great deal of game in spite of its proximity to populated areas. This was Raleigh's domain. His shack was the meeting place for kindred spirits and often times the home for that man who didn't dare do his drinking at his own home. It was a refuge in times of marital storms, the abode of bosom buddies.

Make not too early a poor conclusion
If what you read causes great confusion.
Take all these rich thoughts on kind probation
Until I can prove my dedication.
Diller a Dollar—Ten o'clock scholar,
You take the Diller, I'll take the dollar!

Oh, not again!

GEM

CHICKENS, SUNDAY, AND A RATTLER

This is the part in which is described a most amazing meeting with a terrifying creature and the bold way in which we handled the encounter.

My dear ones,

There was not an ounce of fat on the large body of George Ootman. He was a rugged man, a strong man, and a very large man. He was also a dear hunting pal of Uncle Al and Dad. When away from local restraints, he dearly loved his schnapps. While deer hunting he carried a long, heavy, and very ancient gun which he seldom fired, but if he did, a slug from this piece of antiquity was expelled with enough force to easily bowl over an elephant.

George and his wife came to call on us one Sunday evening in the early fall. They came to arrange to buy some twenty-week-old, ready-to-lay pullets which we had raised for just this purpose. The discussion of this purchase, or, for that matter, any business on Sunday was considered highly improper in our neighborhood, an unforgivable sin. We knew why the Ootmans had come to call, and they, of course, knew the reason. However, nary a word of this errand was, in deference to strong local reli-

284

gious customs, mentioned. Thus it was that we engaged in a rambling, desultory conversation which ranged back and forth from the weather to the sight of the first fall flock of wild Canada honkers to farm crops in general (George was an orchard man) and, because he was an old timer, he could also give us some history of River Roost. We also talked about snakes because on a chicken farm snakes are seldom seen, for if one should accidentally wander into a chicken yard it would be quickly and savagely pecked to death. Oh, we had recently seen, between the house and the barn, near two ancient oak trees, a small blow snake that was trying to swallow a bullfrog. On seeing us, it promptly regurgitated the frog and wriggled away into the tall grass. The frog also hopped away. These harmless blow snakes could extend their heads into a frightening hood, looking every bit as dangerous as a cobra. This snake was the only one that we had seen all year. So, we talked on and on until after we had midnight "coffee" and then were free to negotiate the sale of two hundred pullets. After the culmination of this little business arrangement, George and his wife made motions of leaving. Four steps down from the kitchen a door opened onto our back porch. Our guests descended ahead of us and then moved in the dark out onto a large concrete base. I should have gone ahead, but since I didn't, I rapidly followed as far as the door in order to turn on the yard and porch lights. The switch for these lights was just inside the door. When the lights came on I half-opened the door, preparatory to following our company out to their car for that last chat. It was then that I heard a peculiar sound similar in a weak sort of way to a June bug flapping against the screen in order to gain admittance to a light. Coiled in a corner just outside the door and ready to strike was a Missaukee rattlesnake! With his tail vibrating a warning, his forked tongue darting and his beady eyes reflecting the light from the yellow bulb overhead, my first and, to this date, the last wild rattler I have ever seen, was a shocking sight! And it was on our back porch! How the Ootmans had safely passed inches from this vicious thing, I shall never understand. We now remembered that Rascal, our nondescript dog, had been barking furiously all evening. Darting quickly back and forth with an uncanny judgment of time and distance, Rascal had apparently "worried" the snake into a corner of our porch. We were still ignoring her barking when I switched on the yard lights. Instinctively, I slammed the screen door and stared witlessly at the coiled thing of horror just inches from the door. Fortunately, leaning next to the door was the boys' baseball bat. This I carefully passed out of a window to George, who with supreme disdain and nonchalance bashed in the head of the offending rattler.

"Throw it out in the yard and the mate will come around and you can then kill that also," suggested George. "Nothing doing," replied Cecile. "We want no mates. Bury it!" I did, digging a hole two feet deep to do so. The snake had eight rattles and measured somewhat less than three feet in length. The bite from these small rattlers is not quite so serious as the bite from a timber or a diamond-back rattler, but their poison can still make one awfully sick.

Thus endeth my first hard day at the office with a borrowed posture chair, my old typewriter, and a card table.

Ah, yes, I can still hear that rattler's buzz!

GEM.

LUCKY, THE LAMB

Disclosing how Uncle Al entered upon a new phase of animal husbandry, and how certain ladies of uncertain virtue refused to accept the responsibilities of married life by neglecting their children, whereby that responsibility devolved upon one whose true design followed less arduous patterns.

My dear ones,

Uncle Al was a busy man, removing from the basement of the barn a two-year accumulation of that precious, rich, and a trifle aromatic organic material, and placing it, load after jeep load on his 1970 project, his dream garden. This project entailed much slow and arduous labor which he had entered upon with an enormous enthusiasm not at all shared by Aunt Ruth, who by using the most thinly veiled of excuses of being too busy on some other project, managed to evade his requests for assistance.

This prelude is only to tell how the barn doors were left wide open on that near-zero night in early March when a couple of our ewes decided that this would be an ideal night to lamb! One ewe was too soon with too little and so her lamb was stillborn. The other ewe, however, brought forth into the world a steaming, shivering, tiny buck, using the wide-open door as her maternity ward. There the new lamb stood, quivering, straddle-legged, neglected and wet, by the side of a mother who was either too dumb or too lazy to clean up this frightened and shocked little animal who was so cold that he made no attempt to find his first breakfast.

The most important meal for any animal is his first one. The offspring must receive this first feeding of colostrum, the first milk secreted by the mother, in order to start life with all digestive organs properly functioning. Without colostrum most animals will usually die. Uncle Al bundled up this tiny new bit of life and brought it to the house where an attempt would be made to fulfill those functions and responsibilities which the new mother had failed to undertake. The poor fellow was barely breathing when I placed him in a box of shredded paper in the warmest corner of our kitchen. While I was cleaning and wiping dry this little lamb, Uncle Al with an intuitive flash of genius rushed back to the barn and, catching that neglectful ewe who had spurned her maternal duties, set the creature back on her rump, and he milked her! This first milk we put in a baby bottle and, after having warmed it, taught the lamb what a nipple was for. After this first meal our charge began to show some interest in his strange surroundings, and I was on my way to being the mother of Lucky, for he was lucky to be alive. A little later Al carried him back to the barn again, and amid the violent protests of the lamb's natural mother, he succeeded in putting the ewe back again upon her rump, and thus the little buck was able to have two more feedings. After this, Lucky took up his abode in the box in our kitchen, where at regular intervals I gave him his bottle. These first feedings were spaced every hour and a half at first with Lucky gulping down from four to six ounces of milk. The time between these feedings grew to two hours and then to three hours. As you may have guessed, the quantities of milk consumed also grew in proportion to the length of time between feedings. I began to think that this was going to be very expensive meat; even now I shudder at the thought. After the first few days, I added baby cereal to his milk to give him a more balanced diet; and balance his diet I did, to such an extent that he had diarrhea. His box became very messy indeed and very strong smelling as well. Mr. Lucky was most particular about his box, pawing the litter aside so that he might have a dry place to sleep. I would guess that I was pushing the milk pretty fast because I realized that it was two weeks before he learned to bleat. He didn't have to, for I anticipated his every wish. Everyone remarked at how fast he grew. They also remarked that as he grew so did the odor emanating from his box, even though his foster mother cleaned his restricted area at regular intervals. Apparently it wasn't regular enough.

An impasse, you will perceive, had been reached. Either Lucky had to move, or I had to move, or so I was told in no uncertain words. I wanted to stay. To resolve this difficulty, I finally moved this bouncing boy to the back porch where his aroma was dissipated in the spring breezes. I am now teaching him to eat grain and hay, albeit without too much success, for in his opinion, there is no substitute for milk, which he is now consuming in enormous quantities from twenty-four ounce former grape-juice bottles. On the porch he can jump to his heart's content, but he misses my almost constant attention. He is quite unhappy when someone else attempts to take over his care. As soon as possible, I will attempt to move this delightful fellow out into the field with the other sheep, who, as I know from past experience, will have nothing at all to do with him. This creature, who may look like a sheep, smells like a human to them. Right now, I am delayed by what I hope is the last storm of the season. This March storm has already given us thirteen inches of wet, heavy snow. A high wind has also suddenly descended upon us and is piling the clean white swirling stuff into impassable drifts. Over the protests of my wife and darling daughter, I have been forced to move Lucky back into the kitchen for the duration of this unseasonable, but beautiful storm. What to do, what to do? All I have ever wanted out of life is to be able to keep out of trouble.

All of this has come to you from the very concerned, captive and careful, but challenged, disillusioned, and yet always trying to be helpful, Sage of River Roost, who at this time says, "It sure is nice to have your very own nativity scene."

The Strunk family kindly offered to babysit Lucky for us while we went "gadding" over the weekend to Aunt Selma's house. They naturally fell in love with that perfect gentleman, Lucky, and now would like to keep him, at least until the fall. We have agreed to this, so now Lucky will continue to be spoiled.

Hoo boy, it still smells a bit like Lucky!

GEM

A COLD AND BLUSTERY WEDDING

Sometimes it is very difficult to get through to the right person in this letter-writing task without some officious and snoopy parents trying to read private correspondence. They have not yet learned that a letter is a personal and inviolate thing, especially when a loving grandfather wishes to pass along news of a very special event as well as give some treasured advice to his firstborn granddaughter on the occasion of her first birthday. We will have to forgive their snoopy souls as I am sure they will be reading over your tiny shoulder about the tale of a very special wedding.

My dear Susan,

Since I last wrote to your mother and dad, it has occurred to me that they most likely have not made clear to you all the details of your Aunt Kay's wedding. They probably didn't even discuss it with you, little realizing how important these things are to little people; and so let me review for you a very wild and memorable week in our lives.

I first learned about this coming event while I was in Butterworth Hospital in Grand Rapids recovering from a big operation in my tummy. Picture, if you will, a semi-private room at about 8:15 in the evening, just fifteen minutes before the end of visiting hours. Your grandmother and your Aunt Kay came walking rapidly into the room and without so much as a "by your leave," "zoom" went the dividing curtain in order to create a questionable privacy. Whoever heard of privacy in a hospital? You, little one, should know all about that. The expressions on the faces of these two ladies, ludicrous, sad, worried, hopeful, irritated, and wondering, told me at once that they had come to discuss with me a great event in your Aunt Kay's life.

Ah, those readable countenances! What they didn't realize was that I already knew why they were there; in fact, I was awaiting this call. You must realize that Aunt Kay had had her secret plans for an elopement detected; she didn't realize that marriage licenses are considered vital statistics and that they are printed in the local newspapers! So, you see, the coming event had already cast its shadow and I had already been apprised of the facts from many sources, even by my nurses. It seems that Aunt Kay, feeling that the sadly impoverished condition of your grandparents, due to my long and expensive illness, could neither afford a continuance of her college education or, what to her was more important at the time, a formal wedding, and so she had decided to elope with your soon-to-be Uncle Stan. She didn't want to start her new life heavily in debt. Their secret plans had been in the making for weeks and an apartment in Holland had already been rented. The shock of the publicity of your Aunt Kay's private affairs and the shock of your Grandmother because Aunt Kay had not confided in her produced copious tears which were spilled all around. But finally happiness was restored and your Aunt Kay was relieved to agree to a quiet home wedding at River Roost on the following Sunday, January 20, 1963, for, you see, this is what she really had wanted all along.

Naturally, I wanted to attend this event since I was the father of the bride. So I went right to work on my doctors in the hope that I might be released from the hospital much earlier than normal, and this I did in the happy hopes of giving my daughter away. Now this getting out of a hospital, Susan, strange as it may seem, is not nearly as easy as getting in! I had several obstacles in my path, the first of which was a Foley tube, which is a special type of catheter which is inserted into the bladder so that you don't have to go to the potty. I've often wondered why these tubes weren't used on little people! It would be such a saving of diapers to say nothing of avoiding irritating skin rashes. Quite a handy device! There were three or four surgeons (surgeons are in reality only good mechanics who use a knife rather than a wrench and sometimes consider themselves nearly gods) in attendance upon me who made daily calls. As they made their morning rounds, I started making my requests for the removal of the Foley tube as the first step toward my release.

"Oh, quite impossible,"

"No, of course not," agreed the second man in white. "No, indeed!"

"Impractical and much too dangerous," stated the third. "If something should go wrong, it might necessitate an emergency operation at three or four o'clock in the morning."

Nevertheless, I continued to turn on the pressure, first with the doctors and then with the nurses. Somewhere along the line I must have said the correct thing because somebody weakened and an order came through about 4:30 that afternoon for the removal of my much-discussed Foley. After this rather irritating and uncomfortable procedure was performed, I drank the fastest two quarts of water any individual had ever imbibed. Thus I proved that I was still quite normal and still had very good control!

The next morning I carried my campaign a step further. "How about removing my stitches and discharging me?" I asked the first of the great doctors who called on me.

"Go home? Impossible for several days. I'll tell you what I will do, though; I'll remove half of the stitches for you," which he then did.

There was a flat "NO" from the second surgeon, but when the third one came into the room, I was beaming smiles.

"I am happy to see you!" I exclaimed.

"Why especially so happy to see me?" was the answer.

"Because I just know that you made a very special trip to remove the rest of my stitches and to write an order for my release," I suggested hopefully. "Hmm, I don't know about that. Roll over and let me see your incision. Nurse, the tray, please. Looks good." Zip, zip went the remaining stitches and a new protective bandage was applied. "I don't see why you can't go home if you will follow instructions, wear a binder, etc., etc. Call for an appointment next Wednesday."

"Thanks, Doctor. You don't know what this means to me," I gasped, still a bit weak from that quick stitch removal.

So, the barriers gradually fell, one by one. There was still the office to contend with, a matter of blood to replace that which had been used in my transfusion. I soon discovered that your grandmother had already taken care of this through the Allegan County Red Cross. I was wheeled back from the office to the nurses' station on my floor where I called your Great-Aunt Sylvia, bless her efficient soul, to tell her the news and to plead for further assistance. She was a nurse on the floor directly beneath us, where she was taking care of new babies. (You see, dear Susan, most newborn babies make their worldly appearance in a hospital, not in their daddy's car on the way there!) Foreseeing the many problems that must arise with a wedding but two days in the offing, I asked her if it would be possible for her to get a substitute for Saturday. Fortunately, however, she had that weekend off and agreed to not only drive me home the forty miles, but also to spend Saturday and Sunday helping us. So at 3:30 Friday afternoon, still in her nurse's uniform, Great-Aunt Sylvia, accompanied by your kissing cousins, Carol and Terry, and your very weak granddad started through the snow-packed streets of Grand Rapids enroute to River Roost. Tons of that white stuff had already fallen that January, but nevertheless this particular Friday was a beautiful day with not a single warning of events to come. In spite of all the excitement, I was indeed happy to be on my way home and what was more important, to arrive there warm and safe.

It was this same Friday evening that your Aunt Kay,

very embarrassed and flustered, called her brother, your own dear dad, to tell him about the wedding and to shock him no end, so he later said. Such a rushing to and fro, my darling Susan, you can't possibly conceive. Telephone calls to make. Cakes to bake and ice cream to order! Flowers to buy! Hams to cook! A thousand and one details to take care of and just one day to take care of it all. The minister to call! Dresses to be bought! "No, the bride can't wear a black dress for the wedding! Carol can wear it as the bridesmaid," this from your grandmother. Hats and shoes to buy, not to mention all those soft, silk items that go under and out of sight of the dresses! Such a flurry, such a yammering and a clacking you couldn't imagine. It lasted all through Saturday. Great-Aunt Selma also came out to lend her valued assistance. My advice on this or that was sought and then hurriedly ignored and cast aside, which made me wonder why I was consulted in the first place. I was only Aunt Kay's father!

Well! Sunday finally came and such a glorious, sunshiny morning it was. That beautiful sun shining on the glistening snow gave the tremendous effect of a fairy winter wonderland for which Michigan is so famous. Alas, that early morning sun was the last we were to see of it for many days to come. By ten o'clock it was snowing and the wind was blowing at the rate of 30 miles an hour, but it was to get worse, much worse. The storm had started! The wedding was set for 2:30 that afternoon.

Your Great-Uncle Al had come out early Sunday morning driving his Jeep with a snow plow attached to the front. He was going to clear the yard to make room for the many cars of the expected guests. Cousin Terry loaded the porch with wood which he had had to dig out of a snow bank. This wood was to make a blazing fire in the fireplace before which the ceremony was to be performed. Within the house there was still the flurry of the rushing to and fro, much of it quite aimless with last-minute preparations and phone calls. I'll long remember the total of that January phone bill!

The storm continued to worsen with the snowfall more heavy and the wind higher in velocity. Your new Uncle-to-be Stan called to inform us that he was snow-bound and asked what he should do. His home was three miles north of Zeeland. He had called the County Road Commission, but they had flatly refused to plow him out while the storm lasted. "Not a big enough emergency," they said! After several phone calls to us wondering what he should do, my advice was finally followed and he called a wrecker. Ah, me! The wrecker got stuck and had to call another wrecker to pull out the first wrecker. It was bitter cold and the drifts were getting higher. What with all the plows and wreckers and great-aunts and great-uncles and Uncle-to-be Stan, it must sound a bit confusing. It was! Even with tearful Aunt Kay and Carol in the bedroom upstairs, it was quite amusing, too!

Brr! The wind velocity grew higher and higher, tossing the increasing quantity of snow as it fell into ever-greater drifts. The windchill index fell as the storm grew in intensity. Drifts piled up on other drifts, all driven by a wind which by now was even sifting snow under our living room door! Finally, with the help of two wreckers, this Uncle-to-be Stan finally got hauled into Holland at about six P.M., where he showed up at Great-Aunt Selma's house, thoroughly chilled through and shaking like a toy skeleton which hangs in the rear window of some cars, a very nervous and disappointed groom. They had the groom, we had the bride.

I am of necessity getting ahead of myself in this saga of wind and snow. Back at the River Roost, Great-Uncle Al with the help of Great-Uncle Leonard had started for Hamilton about 11:30 in the morning in order to plow a road for the incoming guests and, if necessary, to lead them back through the snow drifts to the farm. In the meantime, Dale Ann, a close friend of Aunt Kay, called from Hamilton where her father had dropped her off because we had assured her that someone would meet her.

Snow In The Woods

She was told to watch for a red Jeep with a plow in front which would be parked in the lot next to the Ford Garage and she could ride out in that.

"But," her voice quavering on the telephone, "I just saw a red jeep heading for Holland on M-40." She was right! Great-Uncle Al had decided that because of the bitterness of the storm that he would go to his home in Holland and attach the bottled gas tanks to his Cree coach so that if the incoming guests couldn't make it, he would be able to transport them in warmth and comfort inside the Cree Coach, which was an abbreviated motor home designed to fit on the back of a pickup truck. This was a wee bit of bad guessing, for while he was doing this, he was completely and most thoroughly snowed out himself! The drifts of snow were now so high, twelve to fifteen feet in places, that they were impassable and even his snow plow couldn't faze them! He was stuck!

At our request Cousin Merlin had picked up your great-great-grandfather early in the morning at Conklin, and with Great-Aunt Lena and Nadine and her children, they had made it as far as Hamilton and even a bit further, where they became stuck in a twenty-foot drift in front of Bowcamps, a shirt-tail relative of your dad's. Oh yes, they were indeed stuck most properly. That also was as far as the Jeep was able to go. By this time, Dale Ann was a

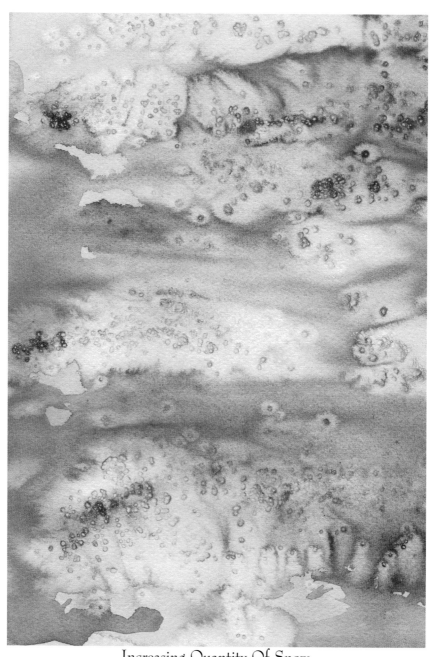

Increasing Quantity Of Snow

member of this party and they all spent the night at Bowcamps, or rather divided between Bowcamps and their next-door neighbor, the Billets.

The heavy fall of snow coupled with the high winds made visibility zero. You see, those roads which run north and south, almost parallel to Lake Michigan only a few miles off to the west, get these unrelenting fingers of snow blowing constantly across them so that even if a plow goes through, those icy fingers build the drifts up again almost as quickly as you can glance behind you. The minister had left Holland at one P.M. and he made it as far as the big curve just at the edge of the city, where he became stalled in a huge drift. Your Great-Uncle Walter almost piled into him and was also stalled. Behind him Walter Jr. came to a sudden forced stop. He, however, with some help managed to maneuver around and to get everyone to the home of Great-Uncle Jim back in Holland. The other cars were simply left in the road. By this time the Michigan State Police closed M-40 and US-31 to all traffic. There were thirty accidents between Holland and South Haven within a period of twenty minutes! The rest of the incoming guests gave up at Holland and returned home wherever it was possible to do so. And so here we were out at River Roost, snowbound in the middle of the forest with a very tearful bride, but with no groom and no minister, two very

305

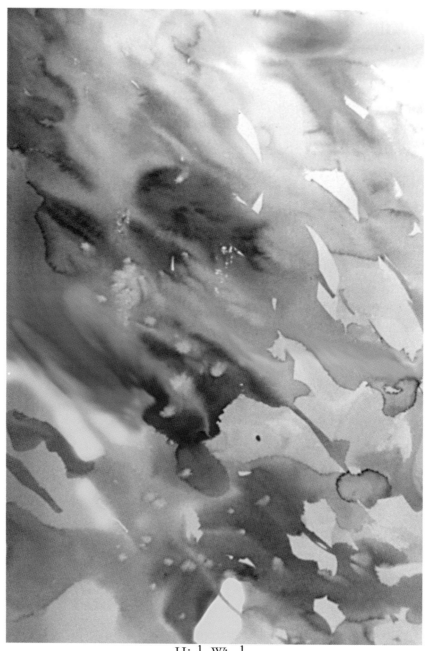

High Winds

important people when a wedding is planned!

From out of the sorrowful depths of sobs and tears an agreement was finally reached to postpone the wedding until the following Thursday evening at 8 P.M. A reception for that date had already been planned, which was to be held at the Holland Country Club where the groom held the dignified title of chef. What choice had the unhappy bride? The decision made, Aunt Kay brightened up and took the storm in stride, even beginning to laugh at some of the amusing incidents of being "stuck!" as the news trickled in. The only change in her plans was that the reception would now follow the wedding ceremony.

Now let's move up to the events of Wednesday night. Your grandmother had made arrangements so that she would not have to work on Thursday in order that she might devote the entire day to Aunt Kay and to her plans, for you see, what had started out as a simple home wedding had now become a church wedding with ushers and bridesmaids and all the rest of the incidentals which go into making up an affair of this order. It was originally planned that only Cousin Carol would be a bridesmaid, but now there would be three, Carol, Dale Ann, and Ilse who was Aunt Kay's roommate from Hope College. Uncle-to-be Stan's brothers would be groomsmen.

In order to avoid any further hitch in the plans,

your grandmother, Carol, and Myrna Lee left River Roost about seven Wednesday evening for Holland so that they would be sure to be there on Thursday, to take care of all the details. This drive usually takes about fifteen minutes. One half hour after they had left, Great-Aunt Selma called to inform us that a special news bulletin over the radio had announced that M-40 and US-31 were again closed to all traffic and she warned us that the folks on our end should stay put and not attempt to come into Holland. It was storming again, even worse, if that were possible, than on Sunday. Since Grandmother and her helpers had already left, all that I could do was to wait impatiently and to worry with ulcer-making intensity. Driving in a snowstorm with zero visibility can be a most dangerous affair, but driving a 1950's Nash with windows frosting over inside and out in such a storm was a har-rowing experience for them. Finally at 9 PM Grandmother called from my brother's home, your Great-Uncle Jim, to tell me that she had finally made it after two hours on the road. She had gone off the road twice and was about to abandon the car in the blinding snow when she was rescued by National Guardsmen. So with one of the guardsmen driving our car because your grandmother was too chilled and too nervous to drive, and following a National Guard truck, the cavalcade finally made it into

Holland with everyone very, very cold. Myrna Lee, who kept saying, "I'm warm enough and I don't need a scarf," froze her ears. Your shivering and nervous grandmother about this time welcomed a wee "nip."

The wedding finally took place at Zion Lutheran Church in Holland on Thursday evening, January 24, with your Great-Uncle Bud giving the bride away, for you see, I was now the one snowed in, or perhaps, I should say "snowed out," as were also all of the out-of-town guests. They told me that it was a very beautiful wedding with the bride and her bridesmaids very attractive in their white or black sheath dresses. Poor Dale Ann, who after being marooned overnight the previous Sunday, was now "snowed out" again and was unable to be a bridesmaid. More tears! Incidentally, your great great-grandfather who was with the Sunday night marooned party, fell in love, so to speak, with Dale Ann, saying, "She was a real sport and quite a little lady."

Now, my dear Susan, this is the wedding that we all remember and I am sure that each one of those participants has a varying version according to their own experience. A few words of love and advice for you to consider when that very special time of life comes for you: Remember that wedding notices are printed in newspapers for the whole world, especially for your friends and relatives, to see. Never try to elope without first telling your mother because, believe me on this, she will want to be there for your wedding no matter what comes. Wedding plans can go astray due to all kinds of unforeseen situations, and no amount of tears shed over them can change a single thing about that. Oh, and one last piece of advice that I'm sure we will hear at the Roost for years to come: please don't choose January for your wedding month!

I realize that the reading of this letter must, of necessity, have been quite a task, what with certain adults leaning over your shoulder all of the time, trying to get a glimpse of what does not concern them. But forgive them please, for I assure you, they will improve with time. Remember that this is their first experience in the parental role. Even your dear grandmother, with all of her world of experience with little people, still has a tendency to take a peek at someone else's special mail! Here she comes again.

All my love,
Grandpa Glenn

BREAKING RECORDS

Oh, my goodness! Come, look out the window! You won't believe this! Do the children have to go to school today?

My dear ones,

There is that immutable law which says that at certain times of each year this area will break a record, weather-wise. One year it will be the greatest snowfall, the next year it will be the greatest rainfall or the largest hail stones seen since our white angora Cleo was a kitten. This year is no different. Now we have a condition which has to go down in the record books as the year of the mud! The wettest mud, the stickiest mud, and the most mud now covers our roads. The earliest and the warmest spring in memory has arrived, causing the frost to leave the ground, and all the snow to melt on only one day. Mud, mud everywhere and not a spot to place a dry foot. Between the blacktop road to Hamilton and the edge of our north woods there now is a lake where none was ever before. This lake straddles our gravel road and is now six inches deep because no provision was ever made for water to flow under the road, and the bottom has completely dropped out. It is thus necessary for me to take the children for a precarious ride in the ancient Buick through terrific ruts, filled with ice water and mud, all the way from the farm to the end of the woods. From there they can walk the rest of the way to their one-room schoolhouse by walking through the adjacent cornfields and thus bypassing the muddy road. I don't dare drive my nice, new, brown, gleaming station wagon because of those gooey roads—the worst since we moved to River Roost! Oh, to be a little bird and fly from here to there. I can't even imagine those drought-like days to come with their dusty, dry roads just now.

GEM

A TALE OF A SALE

This is the tale of the strange, unpremeditated, unhappy sale of River Roost.

My dear ones,

It was early one Monday evening, I think, while I was most comfortably ensconced on the davenport with a heating pad at my back watching TV when our back doorbell rang (yes, we had a back doorbell), and shortly thereafter, Cecile ushered into our living room a young man who introduced himself as William (Bill) W..., an engineer of the Prince Manufacturing Corporation, who had recently been transferred to Holland.

"I was driving around looking for possibilities, and your farm looks like a fine place to raise a family," he told us. "I have five children and we need a lot of room both inside and outside. Would you consider selling?" At that moment, this was the farthest thing from my mind, but since his question demanded some sort of an answer, I became coy and my response was simple and to the point. "Perhaps, if we could be tempted by a price which seems large enough."

After Cecile had shown him through the house, he made us an on-the-spot offer of $35,000. While leaving the door open for future negotiations, I told him that his offer was not nearly enough.

"Well," he wondered, "would you mind if I brought my wife and family out to look at the farm on Saturday?" This he did, giving our home another thorough inspection which ended with the query, "Have you given any further thought to the price?" My answer was the same as on his first call, except we had to have fifty big ones and that price was firm. So, after telling us that they thought that our price was too high, the W... family left. I think that our kitchen was not modern enough for Mrs. W...; there was no dishwasher or clothes dryer or other modern necessities. We thought that the matter was closed and settled back into our usual routine. About ten days later, in the evening, Mr. W... drove into our yard and coming to the door professed that the reason for his call was to give us his phone number where he could be reached should we change our minds on the price. Again, I assured him that our price was firm and after asking him to come in, I tried to explain our reasons for the stiff (was it?—after looking around, we wondered) price. I thought of some beauties. A life of sales work doesn't exactly leave one with a mental vacuum. "Well," he guessed, "if I can convince my wife that I will modernize the kitchen (I was right!), I think that we will take it." The following Monday evening he was back to present us with a check—earnest money until we could draw up a "Buy and Sell" agreement. This has since been signed and we are now engaged in looking, so far with little success, for a nest to house our belongings and a place to lay our weary heads. Twenty-three years of sentiment was hovering over me; so before the agreement was signed, I ruthlessly began to point out all the faults in our property with the faint hope that he might change his mind, but it was to no avail. Whether we made a wise decision, I still do not know, but with my "ouchy back" condition, the sales arrangement will give us a comfortable income along with Social Security, and this financial security was very difficult to refuse.

Now we are faced with the momentous job of finding a place to move into before June first. What will it be? Large or small? Dispose of some of our things or keep them all? When you come to help us move, as suggested by Stan, in a huge moving bee, you will notice a hole in the ceiling where Myrna Lee "hit the roof," going completely through, when she received the news of the sale of the only home she has ever lived in. Underneath the hole, there is still a large unevaporated pool of tears which she shed while Cecile and I looked silently on with monstrous lumps in our throats.

All of this verbiage is to explain that I most probably will be remiss in sending out my little letters to you for the next few weeks because I will be busy,

very, very busy,
Glenn

Acknowledgements

This project is the story of a family, the McNitt family, and it would not have been possible without the contributions of many family members. My greatest debt is to my late Uncle Glenn for his literary talent and his foresight in writing the original letters to the extended family. It was his dream to have his "Historie of River Roost" published one day. Many years ago when I was a child, I asked him who wrote all those books in his extensive library. He said, "People just like you. Maybe one day you will write a book." As I typed out the stories, I often could hear his voice in my ears or see his smile when I checked out a peculiar word in the dictionary. His stories are no longer in boxes and I know he would be pleased. My Aunt Cecile's contribution to this work was that she simply lived it with her love. She giggled over the stories and one time said, "I don't think anyone else ever made more chicken dinners than I did!" The oldest McNitt child, Glenn, called "Chum" by the family, said recently, "You remember the happy and fun side of the Roost, but you have to remember that I had to leave my third grade classmates in the Grand Rapids school where I was happy. I didn't have friends on the farm and since I was the oldest child, I had to work hard. It wasn't the idyllic place for me as it was for you, but I am fine with that. It's just that I was happy to leave it when I went off to college." I appreciate my cousin's view of those days because there were difficult times which we tend to forget. After reading a few stories, my cousin Ted declared, "This is certainly a labor of love for you!" His comment helped me to define this completed project. It was for the funeral service of my dearest cousin Kay several years ago that the opening lines of this project were written. Kay's too early death was the catalyst for moving this project from an idea into the reality that it is. Her husband Stan, her daughter Kimberly, and her son Michael are a source of encouragement. My youngest McNitt cousin, Myrna, who loaned me many family pictures and documents, has always been one of life's best gifts to me. Myrna is the perfect person to talk with about almost anything. I can't imagine life without the closeness of a cousin like Myrna. When I insisted that there had to be another box somewhere with more stories from Uncle Glenn's manuscripts, we searched the attic, which contained a huge McNitt collection of life's memorabilia. I needed the story of Kay's wedding, which I knew Glenn had written. Finally, she said, "Here it is! Look through this box." Thanks, Myrna, the stories are all here, I also want to thank Aunt Selma Godin, the youngest of the Schwartz sisters; for her loving insistence that these stories be written and handed down to the grandchildren. "If you don't do it, who will?"

Years ago I discovered that my good friend Judy Finnegan painted wonderful watercolors, real subjects with an abstract quality. I knew that I wanted her to illustrate the stories. We spent many hours in conversation and took many trips to the River Roost homestead and the Kalamazoo County Fair pursuing the sense of place upon which the imagery is based. Judy also prepared the layout for publication. We are grateful to her husband, Dr. Jerry Finnegan, for securing the technological equipment which we needed as well as his encouraging comments. My husband, David Eichinger, has also been a source of great encouragement from his helpful editing suggestions to his challenging us with new possibilities.

On our visits to the original homestead Judy and I met Diane Wunder, a daughter of the family who bought the farm from the McNitts. She and her family have remodeled the barn into a house where they now live. When I mentioned the stuffed bear cub that had been left in the house, she immediately went upstairs and carried it down. I was amazed to see it again after so many years. Diane was so intrigued with the writing of the River Roost stories that she took us on a hasty trip in her golf cart through the woods thick with mosquitoes on a summer afternoon to the edge of the Kalamazoo River. The marshland views with summer leaves and flowers, with speckled light sparkling on the water were unforgettable. Thank you, Diane, for letting us photograph your garden and animals and for a lovely afternoon at the farm.

We also thank James Smith who provided us with a plat map that indicated the location of the McNitt property in Allegan County.

This project is supported by ArtServe Michigan in conjunction with the Michigan Council for Arts and Cultural Affairs.

Carol Eichinger
Kalamazoo, Michigan
2001